HOPE, FAITH & HEALING

Consultant: Michael McCullough, Ph.D., Director of Research, National Institute for Healthcare Research

Contributing Writers: Carol Turkington, Candyce Norvell, Kim Campbell Thornton

Publications International, Ltd.

Michael McCullough, Ph.D., is Director of Research at the National Institute for Healthcare Research (NIHR), a non-profit institute dedicated to exploring scientific evidence linking religious commitment and spiritual factors to good health. McCullough is also an assistant adjunct professor of clinical psychology at Fuller Graduate School of Psychology, which is affiliated with Fuller Theological Seminary.

Carol Turkington is a freelance writer and a former editor and writer for the Duke University Medical Center and the American Psychological Association.

Candyce Norvell is a freelance writer whose work has appeared in numerous publications including *Ms.*, *Better Nutrition*, and the *Ann Arbor News*, for which she co-wrote a regular column with the Institute for Psychology and Medicine.

Kim Campbell Thornton is an award-winning writer and editor whose work has appeared in various publications including the *Journal of Emergency Medical Services*.

Editorial Assistance: Sonia Weiss

ACKNOWLEDGMENTS

The publisher gratefully acknowledges the kind permission granted to reprint the following copyrighted material. Should any copyright holder have been inadvertently omitted, they should apply to the publisher, who will be pleased to credit them in full in any subsequent editions.

Excerpts from *Timeless Healing: The Power and Biology of Belief* by Herbert Benson, M.D., with Marg Stark. Reprinted with the permission of Scribner, a Division of Simon & Schuster. Copyright © by Herbert Benson, M.D.

ISBN: 0-7853-2446-1

Library of Congress Card Catalog number: 97-69452

Note: Neither Publications International, Ltd., nor the authors, consultants, editors, or publisher take responsibility for any possible consequences from any treatment, procedure, exercise, dietary modification, action, or application of medication or preparation by any person reading or following the information in this book. The publication of this book does not constitute the practice of medicine, and this book does not attempt to replace your physician or your pharmacist. Before undertaking any course of treatment, the authors, consultants, editors, and publisher advise the reader to check with a physician or other health care provider.

CONTENTS

Introduction

Can hope and faith heal? New research says it can. Your thoughts and attitudes are powerful weapons against disease. Prayer, faith in a higher power, hope, belief in a treatment, and a positive outlook can all influence your health for the better.

Those who live with hope and faith have a better chance of being—and staying—healthy. It's no secret that stress has serious long-term effects on your body. A positive attitude alone can boost your immune system and protect you from stress-related illnesses. Imagine what faith in a higher power can do.

Hope, Faith & Healing explores the latest research and shows you how you can use your thoughts, emotions, and beliefs to complement traditional medicine. A strong sense of faith—and involvement in religion—can result in better overall physical health, prevention of serious diseases including heart disease and cancer, less frequent use of the health care system, fewer and milder symptoms, better recovery when illness does occur, and a longer life expectancy.

Faith is linked to better emotional health, too. People with faith tend to be happier, be more satisfied with their lives and relationships, and have higher self-esteem. Faith also helps to alleviate some mental health conditions, including depression.

Hope, Faith & Healing also shows you how your social connections can mean the difference between life and death. A host of recent studies have highlighted the connection between social support and healing—people who are surrounded by close, loving friends and family members are more likely to survive illness than those who are alone. In fact, simply owning a pet has been shown to increase your life expectancy. (Researchers are just beginning to understand the important roles animals play in combating loneliness and anxiety, especially in those individuals who are elderly and disabled.)

Recent studies also suggest hope, like faith, is an effective way to cope with illness and other kinds of suffering, including grief. How does hope heal? Hope prepares the mind and body to endure suffering and look to the future for better times. Hope keeps the spirit alive and provides the desire for overcoming disease.

Your willingness to take responsibility for your health care—and aggressively seek out treatments—can also have a direct effect on your health. When you are well informed about your health, you can take better care of yourself. Research shows that you will recover more quickly from illness if you understand what caused your condition, how a specific treatment can help, and how certain behavior or lifestyle changes can improve your chances of complete recovery.

Thus, the best kind of medical care involves a partnership between you and your doctor. Gone are the days when the doctor knew best; instead, many of today's advanced medical centers are using a team approach to health care, in which patients are expected to participate. Far from resisting patient involvement, today's modern physicians welcome the input of an educated patient. Hope, Faith & Healing shows you how to become an integral part of the treatment team.

Finally, Hope, Faith & Healing explores how a healing environment can be created with alternative therapies such as music and color therapy, dance therapy, horticulture therapy, aromatherapy, and visualization. And, to patients and doctors searching for a new way of dealing with a problematic illness, alternative therapies may have much to offer.

Maintaining wellness is a lifelong journey. Hope, Faith & Healing shows you how to tap into the power of your heart and mind to keep you well along the way.

CHAPTER 1
Faith and Healing

These days, many of us think of our bodies as machines. When they "break down," we take our broken bodies to modern-day mechanics—our doctors. We expect them to tinker around, to "tune us up," to make us run right again. And, in cases of serious trouble, our doctors may even suggest replacing a part or two.

Recently, though, some doctors have turned their focus to the core of the human body: the soul. Researchers are discovering that the state of the soul has a lot to do with the overall health of the human machine. Good mechanics simply aren't enough. To be wholly healthy, you have to have a strong sense of faith, too.

WHAT HAPPENED TO HEYWARD

On May 11, 1992, Heyward Morris, a 13-year-old Atlanta girl, was rollerblading with a friend. Caught up in the fun, Heyward suddenly skated out of the driveway and right into a moving car.

At the hospital, doctors told Heyward's parents that she had suffered traumatic brain injury and was in a deep coma. The doctors were certain the coma would be permanent; there was nothing more they could do. Heyward's life, as her parents had known it, was over.

Fortunately for Heyward, she lived among people who weren't ready to give up. They began to pray. Heyward's mother, Carter Morris, told Dan Wakefield, author of *Expect a Miracle*, what happened after the accident:

"The word of our daughter's injury had got around the community, and people poured their hearts out. There was a vast network of Christians and non-Christians praying for her. We're not a high-profile family. My husband is an attorney, and we belong to St. Luke's Episcopal Church, but we're not high profile religiously or in the community. Still, the word spread like wildfire. We were deeply moved by the outpouring of prayer and compassion from people we didn't even know. It made us feel that people are good. There were Bible study groups from other churches, there was a group called 'prayer warriors,' there were people from all over, praying their hearts out. At one point I felt there was so much support that the hospital itself could have been raised off its foundations by prayer."

Even Heyward's classmates at her nondenominational private school prayed for her every morning. On the eleventh day of her coma, the kids decided they wanted to pray for something more specific than their friend's recovery. Maybe, in their childlike impatience, they wanted something to happen now. Maybe they wanted a sign that God was listening to them. In any case, they decided to pray that Heyward would open her eyes. According to Heyward's mom, that was the day her daughter awoke from the coma. When Heyward opened her eyes, a stunned doctor asked her if she had so much as a headache. Heyward said no.

Did prayer play a part in the healing of Heyward? Even if it did, the doctors still had plenty of work to do. After two months in a rehabilitation hospital, however, Heyward Morris was well—healed by faith and modern medicine.

MODERN MEDICINE

Chances are, when you are sick, you don't go to see a priest, pastor, or rabbi. If you meet with members of the clergy, it's to seek comfort for your soul. For treatment of physical illnesses, you go to a physician or another trained healer—perhaps a nurse or a chiropractor. In this day and age, the priest no longer plays the role of physician. In fact, the two professions offer very separate services: One focuses on the soul, the other on the body. At one time, however, their services were very much intertwined. Throughout history, spirituality and science have long been partnered in the fight against pain and suffering:

- Archaeologists have uncovered manuscripts, written on papyrus, that describe the use of spiritual incantations in the healing practices of ancient Egypt.

Hope, Faith & Healing

- In ancient India, the healing system was called *Ayurveda*, a word that means "life knowledge." In the book *Hinduism: Its Historical Development*, author Troy Wilson Organ writes, "The origins of Indian medicine are both empirical (scientific) and magical. Some of the medicinal plants were first discovered by watching animals and birds heal themselves by eating certain fruits, seeds, leaves, and roots....Word and symbol magic were also part of the therapy...."

- References to the link between spirituality and medicine are also common in the Bible's Old Testament. "And the LORD spoke to Moses and Aaron, saying: When a man has on the skin of his body a swelling, a scab, or a bright spot, and it becomes on the skin of his body like a leprous sore, then he shall be brought to Aaron the priest or to one of his sons the priests." (Leviticus 13:1–2)

- The practice of praying for healing is also typical of the New Testament (KJV). "And it happened when he was in a certain city, that behold, a man who was full of leprosy saw Jesus; and he fell on his face and implored Him, saying, 'Lord, if You are willing, You can make me clean.' Then He put out His hand and touched him, saying, 'I am willing; be cleansed.' And immediately the leprosy left him." (Luke 5:12–13)

In the New Testament, when Jesus sent out his disciples to tell the world about him, he told them: "And, as you go, preach, saying, 'The kingdom of heaven is at hand. Heal the

Hope, Faith & Healing

sick.'" (Matthew 10:7–8) And the disciples listened and did as they were told. Over the next centuries, when Christian missionaries went to Africa, Asia, and South America, they preached the gospel *and* built hospitals.

• Faith and healing traveled hand in hand well into early American history. When America was a British colony, its clergymen were also its doctors. That's because medicine was a required subject in the British theology schools of the day. Preachers were expected to be healers.

The partnership between faith and medicine began to unravel as the scientific revolution began in the seventeenth century. With science came many miracles. By the nineteenth century, there were antibiotics that could halt dangerous infections. There were antiseptics to prevent infections during childbirth and surgery. Diseases that once crippled and killed millions could now be prevented with relatively simple immunization procedures.

As time passed, people became more knowledgeable about the human body. Scientists discovered how blood circulates, the existence of bacteria and viruses, and even the building block of the human genome—DNA, or deoxyribonucleic acid. But as they learned more about the physical causes and cures of illness, they grew away from the knowledge that the mind, spirit, and environment all played important roles in the body's health. Dances, chants, and scented plants were labeled

Hope, Faith & Healing

witchcraft or derided as primitive superstition. Drugs and technology held sway over the medical establishment, while ancient natural healing techniques soon fell by the wayside, dismissed as old wives' tales or unproven nonsense.

Until the scientific revolution, healing had always been one part medicine, one part faith. Now it seemed that faith was no longer necessary. George Bernard Shaw, the Irish playwright, born in 1856, observed of the time, "We have not lost faith, but we have transferred it from God to the medical profes-

sion." Medicine accomplished so much, so fast, that for a time it was widely assumed there were no limits to what modern medicine could do—whatever science hadn't yet figured out would be discovered soon enough. After all, if modern science could explain what was once unexplainable—and cure what was once incurable—who needed God?

Over time, society realized that there were limits to what medicine could do. There were some ailments that medicine apparently could not conquer. Debilitating and sometimes deadly viruses continued to afflict society—even when the best of modern medicine was employed. In recent years, scientists have discovered that some of the most dangerous killers in Western culture—heart disease and cancer—are not even caused by viruses or germs, but by factors such as smoking, obesity, and lack of exercise.

Today, however, physicians and other health care practitioners are beginning to realize that medication and surgery are not the only tools necessary to make people well. Insight into the emotional or mental underpinnings of disease is also necessary. More and more it becomes obvious that the link between mind and body is a powerful one, a link that is not easily broken or ignored. With this realization comes the acceptance of some alternative therapies as effective adjuncts to modern medicine.

The Face of Faith in America

Here is a statistical snapshot, taken in 1994, of Americans and their religious beliefs:

Responding to a Gallup poll, 87% said they were Christian (53% Protestant, 26% Catholic, 8% other), 2% said they were Muslim, 2% said they were Jewish, 2% followed other religions (Hinduism, Buddhism, etc.), and 7% had no religion.

Overall, African-Americans are the most religious ethnic group, women are more religious than men, and older people are more religious than younger people.

Hope, Faith & Healing

Science plays an important part in the healing process, but without faith, can healing really be complete? Many individuals have not abandoned the role of faith in healing. Instead they have become frustrated with the medical profession—and its lack of interest in spirituality. As a result, many people have turned to alternative healers and practices—herbalism, yoga, meditation, hypnosis, aromatherapy. A study reported in *The New England Journal of Medicine* in 1993 found that one-third of all Americans had used alternative healing methods, spending nearly $14 billion on these practices every year.

THE PATIENTS

Can an individual's attitude and religious beliefs have an impact on the healing process? New research shows the key to healing may indeed lie in the hands of the patient, and not in the minds of scientists.

According to a Gallup poll published in 1990, 95% of Americans believe in God. And, according to the poll, nearly three-quarters of Americans agree with the statement, "My whole approach to life is based on my religion." Gallup also reports that 42% of Americans attend religious services regularly.

A 1996 *USA Weekend* poll found that 79% of Americans believe that faith plays a role in helping people recover from illness or injury. Many of these people ground their belief in personal experiences: 56% said they have experienced the healing power of religious faith in their own lives.

And Americans are not just believers. They are also pray-*ers*. A 1993 survey by the Barna Research Group found that nearly 90% of Americans say they pray to God, and 60% pray more than once a day. A 1996 Time/CNN poll found that more than 75% of Americans believe that God sometimes heals people who are seriously ill, and 73% believe that praying for others can help speed their recovery.

In a study published in 1991 on the helpfulness of prayer, 96% of patients facing heart surgery said they prayed. Similarly, a study reported in 1994 found that 73% of hospitalized patients prayed.

A survey published in 1986 found that one of every seven people polled believed that, at some point, he or she had been healed by God; the miraculous cures occurred for all types of illnesses—everything from simple viruses to debilitating back pain to cancer.

So, not only do most Americans believe in God, they believe in a *healing* God. And research provides ample evidence that Americans want their doctors to acknowledge this belief. The *USA Weekend* poll found that 63% of Americans think it's a good idea for doctors to talk with patients about the role faith plays in healing. And, according to the Time/CNN poll, 64% said doctors should pray with their patients when the patients ask them to. In the 1990 Gallup poll, 77% of respondents said doctors should consider the spiritual needs of the patients, and 48% wanted their doctors to pray with them.

THE DOCTORS

In the *USA Weekend* poll, although 63% of Americans said doctors should talk with their patients about faith, only 10% said their doctors had actually done so. The same poll also

showed that 90% of physicians don't want to mix religion and spirituality with medicine. The results of the poll are not surprising—research shows that fewer than half of all medical doctors feel close to God.

This patient-doctor dilemma is vividly illustrated in a 1991 study of Vermont family practitioners and their patients. The study results showed that only 64% of the doctors believed in God, compared to 91% of the patients. Only 45% of the doctors who participated in the study believed in an afterlife, compared to 60% of the patients. And approximately 60% of the doctors prayed on a regular basis, compared to 85% of the patients.

How do psychiatrists and psychologists feel about faith and healing? When Gallup polled members of the American Psychiatric Association about their spiritual beliefs, 57% of respondents said they had none. When Gallup asked psychologists and psychiatrists whether they agreed with the state-

Hope, Faith & Healing

ment, "My whole approach to life is based on my religion," 67% of psychologists and 61% of psychiatrists said no.

In fact, in the past, some members of the mental health profession have actually referred to religious faith as a mental illness. This viewpoint may be traced back to the research of Sigmund Freud, who once said, "Religion is comparable to a childhood neurosis." In fact, Freud called religion a "universal obsessional neurosis"—a mental illness with which the entire human race may be afflicted. For some time, Freud's opinions remained one of the predominant opinions of the mental health profession.

But some of the twentieth century's most brilliant scientists thought otherwise. Albert Einstein said, "Science without religion is lame; religion without science is blind." And a small but outspoken number of physicians and other scientists agreed with him. Today, many doctors see firsthand how faith works—and that it's foolish to ignore its potential. These doctors are learning how to use faith—their own and their patients'—to aid in healing.

THE RESEARCH: WHAT SCIENCE SAYS

The results of scientific studies on faith are just beginning to come in, and they are exciting. Study after study affirms that faith is good medicine, says Dale A. Matthews, M.D., an associate professor of medicine at Georgetown University School of Medicine, a senior research fellow at the National Institute for Healthcare Research, and a practicing internist. In an issue of *Mind/Body Medicine* that was devoted to spirituality and medicine (Vol. 2, No. 1, 1997), Matthews wrote: "When studied scientifically, religious commitment has been generally found to have significant health benefits. In a review of more than 200 published studies of the linkage between religion and health status, 75% revealed a positive relationship."

A strong sense of faith—and involvement in religion—can result in better overall physical health, fewer and less severe symptoms, prevention of serious diseases including heart disease and cancer, less use of the health care system, and better recovery when serious illness does occur. Faith is linked to better emotional health: People of faith tend to be happier, be more satisfied with their lives and relationships, and have higher self-esteem. Faith also helps to alleviate some mental health conditions, including depression and anxiety. Finally, people of faith are less likely to have sexually transmitted diseases, probably due to lower rates of extramarital sexual activity.

Clearly, there is healing power in faith.

Wrote Matthews in *Mind/Body Medicine*, "I do not encourage or demand patients to practice religion simply because I am a religious person and believe, as a matter of faith, that religion is good for your health (although both of those statements are true). As a believer in the scientific method, an orthodox medical practitioner, and a medical school professor, I believe that the medical value of faith is not a matter of faith—but of science. The scientific evidence of the health benefits of religious practice justifies its consideration in medical practice."

THE STUDY OF FAITH

Nearly all the studies of the role of faith in healing have fallen into one of three categories: the role of religious faith in general, the role of prayer in health and healing, and the role of religious participation in health and healing.

THE ROLE OF FAITH

It seems that people who are deeply religious are more likely to receive the health benefits of faith than people who are not. According to Matthews, there are two principal types of religious orientation: extrinsic and intrinsic. Extrinsics see religion as a way to get something, whether it be health, money, or another desire. Interestingly, research has found that these people are not likely to enjoy better health as a result of their faith.

Intrinsics, by contrast, Matthews says, are people who are "God-oriented, rather than self-oriented." They are not religious because they think that by being religious they can get something. They are religious because they believe that their religion connects them to God. It is these people—those who

Hope, Faith & Healing

seek God for the sake of God—who are most likely to receive the health benefits of faith.

The English writer C. S. Lewis wrote, "In religion, as in war and everything else, comfort is the one thing you cannot get by looking for it. If you look for truth, you may find comfort in the end. If you look for comfort, you will not get either comfort or truth. . . ."

Harold G. Koenig, M.D., an associate professor of psychiatry and behavioral sciences, an associate professor of internal medicine, and director of the Program of Religion, Aging, and Health at Duke University Medical Center, is a leader in research on religious coping. Studies by Koenig and others have found that religious coping can effectively alleviate many of the symptoms of various illnesses.

Religious coping is defined as the use of religious beliefs or behaviors to alleviate the emotional distress associated with psychosocial stress and to facilitate problem solving. In other words, religious coping is applying one's religious faith to the stresses that come with illness.

A person who is diagnosed with a serious, life-threatening illness experiences more than just the physical symptoms of the illness. There are also symptoms related to the stress of the illness, including anxiety, depression, sleeplessness, loss of appetite, pain and discomfort from medical procedures, fear of dying, and loneliness, especially if the person is hospitalized away from family and friends.

Koenig developed the Religious Coping Index (RCI), a three-step process designed to analyze a patient's use of faith in coping with illness. First, the patient is asked what resources he or she uses to cope with illness. The question contains no reference to faith or religion. If the patient's answer includes a reference to religion, the researcher gives that answer a score of 10. An answer with no mention of religion gets a score of 0.

Second, the patient is asked to rate, on a scale of 1 to 10, how much he or she uses religion to cope with illness.

Third, the patient is asked to discuss how he or she uses religion to help cope with illness, and to give a specific example of religious coping. After this discussion, the researcher rates the patient on a scale of 1 to 10, the higher scores reflecting that religion is a very important coping resource for the patient.

The three scores are added; the highest possible score is 30.

Over the course of several studies using the RCI, Koenig and his associates found that 24% to 42% of older patients scored 10 on the first question; that is, when asked how they cope with illness, they cited religion. When asked to rate how much they use religion in coping, 75% of the patients said they used religion at least to a large extent, and 90% said they used it at least to a moderate extent. The RCI studies found that variables such as education, income, and occupation did not directly affect religious coping; these factors did not make patients more or less likely to use religion to cope with their illnesses. The specific medical condition didn't have an impact on coping, either. People were more likely to use religious coping, however, if they were severely ill or disabled, had good cognitive functioning (that is, were able to think clearly), had strong social support, and did not drink alcohol. Patients who became more ill or disabled over periods of time were also more likely to use religious coping. Patients in recovery used religious coping less as they improved.

In studying the effect of religious coping on depression, the researchers found that the more intense the religious coping, the less depressed the patient was. "Specific symptoms of depression (loss of interest, feelings of worthlessness, social withdrawal, lack of hope, etc.) were particularly infrequent among those with strong religious coping strategies," Koenig reports in Mind/Body Medicine. However, religious coping did not have any effect on biological symptoms of depression, such as weight loss and insomnia. This means that, while religious patients may have been suffering from the physical manifestations of depression, they didn't feel as depressed as the nonreligious patients.

"In fact," writes Koenig, "religious coping was the only. . . factor that significantly predicted better mental health outcomes. . . . These are not isolated findings. Numerous investigators, working in different areas of the country, have reported similar findings. These studies suggest that older persons who use religion in this manner experience lower rates of depression, have higher self-esteem, and appear to live longer."

Although studies so far show no link between faith and relief from the physical symptoms of depression, faith has been shown to alleviate the physical symptoms of other illnesses, and to have a very real impact on survival.

- In 1982, studies of Mormon men showed that those who were very religious were less likely to get cancer than less religious individuals. If they did get cancer, religious Mormons had better recoveries than nonreligious Mormons.

- In a study of people who had fractured hips, reported in 1990 by the *American Journal of Psychiatry*, those who were very religious recovered faster and were less depressed by their injuries.

- In a study that followed people for six months after they had heart surgery, the death rate among the deeply religious group was 0% compared to a 12% death rate for people who never—or almost never—went to church. In the study, which was reported in 1995 in *Psychosomatic Medicine*, all the patients in the study were over age 60.

- Another study reported the mortality and life expectancy of Seventh Day Adventists in the Netherlands. This interesting study tracked elderly people for two years after they moved into an institutional setting. Those who were religious were more likely to live for two years after the move

than those who were not religious. The researchers concluded that the religious people must have drawn strength and comfort from their religion.

- In a study of veterans who were hospitalized, the veterans who survived the one-year study period were more likely to be religious than those veterans who died.

- A study of 1,000 university students in Illinois found that highly religious students were healthier than their schoolmates—they suffered fewer injuries and illnesses. In addition, the religious students smoked less, drank less alcohol, and experimented with drugs less often.

MORE THAN THE PLACEBO EFFECT

Some would argue that a study can't validate faith. After all, almost anything a person believes in can, in one way or another, have a positive impact. The power of this "placebo effect" has been illustrated again and again. In the past, for example, there were a variety of treatments for *angina pectoris*, pain in the chest and arms. (One of the more exotic treatments involved injections of cobra venom.) For a time, doctors expected such treatments to work so they assured patients that their conditions would be cured. Up to 90% of the time they were right. But later, as the cause of angina pectoris came to be better understood, doctors soon doubted the reliability of such treatments. The rate of effectiveness dropped as low as 30%.

Is it possible, then, that the healing power of faith is nothing more than the placebo effect?

In his book *Timeless Healing*, Herbert Benson, M.D., associate professor of medicine at Harvard Medical School, writes: "Faith in the medical treatment, faith in the health care provider, and faith in the relationship forged between you and your healer are wonderfully therapeutic, successful in treating 60 to 90% of the most common medical problems. But if you so believe, faith in an invincible and infallible force carries even more healing power."

Benson's earlier book, *The Relaxation Response*, explains a simple technique that he discovered could, among other effects, lower a person's blood pressure and muscle tension. The technique, called *the relaxation response*, requires repeating a word or phrase (or a sound or a muscle activity) for several minutes. Any thoughts that interrupt the repetition are passively ignored. If you practice repeating a word or phrase while ignoring all other thoughts, the physiological effects of slowed heart rate, slowed breathing, decreased blood pressure, and muscle relaxation will follow.

Benson knew the power of the placebo effect: He was not surprised to find that patients who believed most in the technique experienced the greatest benefits from it. But Benson also observed something that he couldn't have predicted. About 80% of his patients, when instructed to choose a pleasant word or phrase to repeat, chose a religious word or a prayer. And, interestingly, those patients benefited even more from the technique than those who simply believed in the technique itself.

In *Timeless Healing*, Benson writes: "I already knew that eliciting the relaxation response could "disconnect" everyday thoughts and worries, calming people's bodies and minds more quickly and to a degree otherwise unachievable. It appeared that beliefs added to the response transported the mind/body even more dramatically, quieting worries and fears significantly better than the relaxation response alone. And I speculated that religious faith was more influential than other affirmative beliefs.

"Our studies demonstrated that people feel an increase in spirituality relatively quickly upon eliciting the relaxation response but that the longer one makes the elicitation part of one's routine, the more these sensations grow. Like the physical rewards we had measured, spirituality also seemed to be cumulative, increasing over time as people regularly elicited the response.

"But what exactly were people experiencing that felt spiritual to them? When we compiled the results, some common themes emerged. People who reported increased spirituality after eliciting the relaxation response described two things

Hope, Faith & Healing

about the experience: 1) the presence of an energy, a force, a power—God—that was beyond themselves, and 2) this presence felt close to them."

Further research proved Benson's speculation to be correct. It was the individuals who "felt this presence" who noted the greatest medical benefits. "Faith in God...seems to be particularly influential in healing because 'God,' by all definitions of which I am aware, is boundless and limitless," Benson concludes. "It is part of our nature to believe in an almighty power lest our health be undermined by the ultimate and dreadful fact—that we may succumb to illness and that all of us must die."

Stephen G. Post, Ph.D., associate director of the Center for Biomedical Ethics at Case Western Reserve University, agrees. In an article in Mind/Body Medicine, he wrote: "As innumerable theologians have indicated, persons wish to protect themselves through the security of daily routines that provide order and control over existence. When illness breaks in—especially severe and disruptive illness—the routine is quickly pushed aside by in-breaking waves of chaos. It is like awakening in the morning to find a flood at the back door that disrupts the veneer of daily order and regularity. During illness, people realize that the routine is ultimately not real because human beings are fragile and subject to contingencies over which they hold no ultimate control. At this point, many patients call out to some higher being in the universe, who, in contrast to our-

The Results Are In

Below are the results of a recent *Newsweek* poll on prayer. The poll of 751 adults nationwide was published in the March 31, 1997, issue of the magazine.

82% say they ask for health or success for a child or family member when they pray

75% ask for strength to overcome personal weakness when they pray

87% say that God answers their prayers

36% never pray for financial or career success

29% say they pray to God more than once a day

25% pray once a day

82% say they believe that God does not play favorites in answering prayers

79% say God answers prayers for healing someone with an incurable disease

73% think prayers for help in finding a job are answered

54% say that when God doesn't answer their prayers, it means it wasn't God's will to answer

82% don't turn away from God when prayers go unanswered

selves, does have things under control. One need not be a believer to recognize the existential value of religion in coping with the illness experience...."

Hope, Faith & Healing

Although the research shows that faith in God is a powerful healer, researchers agree that the studies do not show that believing in one religion has more health benefits than believing in another. Thus, if all forms of faith in God are good for our health, then the healing power of faith is available to everyone, regardless of our particular beliefs.

It is interesting to note that one result of all this research is a better reputation for "faith healing." Of course, there will always be individuals who play on the fears of sick people and promise miraculous cures—often for the sole purpose of making money. But faith really can heal—sometimes miraculously. A person with a fatal disease declares that God is going to heal him, and his illness disappears. You pray for someone who is sick and the person gets well. A growing number of what the medical profession calls "spontaneous remissions"—and the rest of us call "miracles"—have been documented. In fact, one list of documented, unexplained healings lists as many as 3,000 cases.

THE FAITH EFFECT

How does faith make people healthier? The links between faith and emotional health are better understood than the links between faith and physical health.

The religious patients studied by Koenig reported five ways that their faith helped them cope with serious illness. First, these patients said their faith gave them hope, from hope for healing to hope for life after death.

Hope, Faith & Healing

Second, the patients said their faith gave them a sense of control and they believed that an all-powerful God would respond to their prayers. "Patients say they talk to God," Koenig reports in *Mind/Body Medicine*, "turn over their problems into His hands, and trust Him to orchestrate the best possible outcome. They can then stop worrying about their problems, and consequently experience comfort and peace."

Third, the patients said their faith gave them strength to face their illness.

Fourth, the patients said their faith gave them meaning—a way to make sense of their illness and pain. One of the first questions most of us ask ourselves when we become seriously ill or injured is, "Why?" If a patient believes that his or 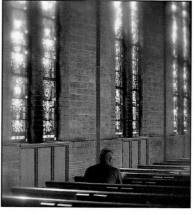 her illness is a punishment from God, the effect can be harmful, causing guilt and increased suffering. But a patient who believes that God allows suffering into people's lives to build their character and help them avoid greater pain in the future can actually find a positive message in pain.

Finally, the patients said their faith gave them a sense of purpose. Koenig gives the example of an elderly woman who was completely paralyzed by a stroke. She could only move her eyelids. The woman's pastor asked her to pray for various people in her church, which she did. Not only did the woman have the satisfaction of being useful, she also was visited by people in the church who told her all the ways in which her prayers were being answered.

"The point of this case," Koenig writes, "is that religious people, no matter how disabled, still possess some small gift or talent that they can use to serve their God."

Hope, control, strength, meaning, and purpose. These things make us feel better; we have all experienced their positive effects. But how can these feelings actually make our bodies healthier? How can feelings of hope and strength cause broken bones to mend, cancer cells to disappear, and painful surgical wounds to quickly heal?

Memories, of course, trigger feelings. But science is now discovering that memories are not just emotional events, but physical events as well. In fact, it seems that the emotions that memories inspire are actually a result of physical changes that take place in the brain.

When you remember a certain event—think of the happiest moment in your life—you feel, more or less intensely, the same emotions you felt at that moment. Why? Research shows that the same pattern of activity occurs in your brain that occurred there when the event first happened. So, in a very real, physical way, your brain reconstructs the event, both emotionally and physically. When you remember a happy event, your mouth may turn up in a smile. When you think of a frightening event, your heartbeat may quicken, even though you know you are no longer in any real danger.

Imagine the power of your brain if it was fueled with feelings of hope, strength, and joy. Could those feelings trigger

How Does Illness Affect Faith?

It's apparent that faith affects illness, but does illness affect faith?

Immanuel Jakobovits, Chief Rabbi of the British Commonwealth of Nations, has written that "disease forges an especially close link between God and man; the Divine Presence Itself, as it were, 'rests on the head of the sickbed.'"

Harold G. Koenig, M.D., director of the Program of Religion, Aging, and Health at Duke University Medical Center, tells of a patient for whom this was exactly so. The 82-year-old man was not religious until after a stay in the intensive care unit (ICU). When asked about his newfound interest in God, the man said that God had appeared at his bedside in the ICU. He remained religious until he died a year later.

Such experiences are not unusual, according to Koenig. In one study, one-third of patients 70 and older said they had a dramatic conversion experience, and nearly half of those said the experience occurred when they were over age 50. For many, the conversion was linked to illness.

activity in the brain that would send signals throughout the body to mend and to heal? If so, this could explain why positive thinking helps to heal, but religious belief is the most powerful healer. Belief in a higher power who is absolutely strong, wise, and loving should be the most powerful belief. It should call forth an unassailable well of hope and strength. And it does. Belief in God, it seems, triggers patterns of brain activity that have intense healing effects on the body.

If this process really works, anyone should be able to unleash powerful healing effects when inspired by religion. Such thoughts should trigger brain activity that produces both positive feelings and physical healing.

There are specific expressions of faith that seem to have the most powerful healing effects. For example, participation in religious rituals is very helpful for some people, because such rituals may bring back strong, positive memories of encounters with God. Prayer is a religious activity that has also shown to be powerfully healing.

The healing power of faith is a wonderful boon, but what about people who don't believe in God? They can experience some health benefits by calling forth positive memories and thoughts that don't involve God. For example, in Timeless Healing, Benson suggests to his nonreligious patients that they may want to repeat words or phrases such as "love," "peace," or "calm." But, as we've seen, people who do involve God in their healing thoughts seem to experience greater health benefits.

Researchers are convinced that certain memories and thoughts trigger similar brain activity in all human beings. For example, research has found that a fear of snakes is virtually universal, although it is stronger in some people than in others. (Most people, in the presence of a snake, experience the familiar physical manifestations of fear: increased heart rate and breathing rate, trembling, and breaking out in a cold sweat.) The other universal triggers we all share are not yet known. Perhaps prayer is one of them.

THE ROLE OF PRAYER

St. Augustine, the great church leader who was born in 354 A.D., wrote that, while miraculous healings did take place at the time of Jesus, such miracles would not continue. These miracles were for one special time in history, Augustine believed, and not for his day or for future times.

Then, in 424 A.D., a brother and sister, both suffering from seizures, came to the town of Hippo in North Africa, where Augustine was bishop. The brother and sister went every day to Augustine's church and prayed that they would be healed. One day, as the brother prayed in the crowded church, he suddenly fell down. When he got up, he was cured of the seizures. The man had been dramatically healed.

Augustine talked with the young man, and soon became convinced that God had, indeed, healed him in answer to his prayers. A couple of weeks later, Augustine placed the man, now healed, and the man's sister, still suffering from seizures, before the congregation. During Augustine's sermon, the young woman, too, was instantly healed.

Augustine began to document the healings that occurred in Hippo. Some of these astonishing miracles were recorded in his great work, *The City of God*. "Once I realized how many miracles were occurring in our  own day... (I realized) how wrong it would be to allow the memory of these marvels of divine power to perish from among our people," he wrote. "It is only two years ago that the keeping of records was begun here in Hippo, and already, at this writing, we have nearly 70 attested miracles."

Today's researchers are also interested in the role of prayer in health and healing. The first important, scientific study of healing prayer was conducted in 1984. Published in 1988, the Byrd Study (named after its lead researcher Randolph Byrd) evaluated the effect of prayer on people who had heart disease. For 10 months, 393 patients who were admitted to the coronary care unit at San Francisco General Hospital were studied.

The patients were divided into two groups. Byrd arranged for people to pray for the patients in one group. The other group served as the control group; as far as Byrd knew, no one prayed for them. And while the patients knew that they were part of a study on prayer, neither they nor medical personnel knew which patients were being prayed for.

The results: Patients who were prayed for did better than patients in the control group. The group of patients receiving prayer had only 27 total complications, compared to 44 complications in the control group. They had 3 cases of pneumonia compared to 13 cases in the control group; 8 cases of congestive heart failure compared to 20 cases in the control group; and 3 cases of cardiac arrest compared to 14 cases in the control group. Prayed-for patients also were less likely to need antibiotics and diuretics. And none of the patients in the prayed-for group had to be intubated, while 12 patients in the control group required this medical procedure. (Intubation is the insertion of a tube to maintain the patient's airway.)

The next major study, reported in 1991, looked at the effects of prayer when patients prayed for themselves. The Saudia Study investigated how prayer could affect patients' feelings, not their physical symptoms. Of 100 patients who were scheduled for coronary artery bypass surgery, 96 prayed for themselves. Two other patients who did not pray had other individuals pray for them; the remaining two patients did not use prayer at all. At the end of the study, 97 of the 100 patients said that prayer had been very helpful to them in coping with the stress of serious illness.

One of the most fascinating studies of the power of prayer didn't even focus on health—or even on people—in the beginning. Karl Goodfellow, a Methodist minister who was working on his seminary doctoral project, ran across some research that showed that corn seeds that were prayed for grew better than corn seeds that received no spiritual assistance. (Although it may seem unusual to some, prayer experiments have been done on all kinds of plants and animals. Like the human studies, those studies have found, generally, that all living things respond positively to prayer.)

The people in Goodfellow's area—most of whom were farmers—began to pray for their corn. Yields increased.

Goodfellow then reached the conclusion that if God cared about corn, He must also care about the people who were growing it. But some of the locals were losing their farms. Others had suffered horrific injuries from pushing themselves to the point of exhaustion. So Goodfellow decided to line up "prayer partners" for every one of the 12,000 farm families in his district. Each prayer partner prayed for 10 farm families, by name, and prayed specifically for increased harvests and safety for those workers.

Larry Dossey, M.D., who summarized Goodfellow's story in his book *Prayer Is Good Medicine*, reports, "Since the prayer project began, farmers have begun to report interesting experiences— 'things that have happened that could have been disasters but weren't.' One farmer was sucked into a gravity wagon of grain, which could have suffocated him, but he was pulled out unharmed. Another farmer near Hawkeye was driving a combine down the road when a semi trailer pulled in front of him. Only a 'miracle' prevented what should have been a fatal collision."

While Goodfellow's experiment started as more of a spiritual project than a scientific one, the University of Iowa is now assisting him in his investigation. Meanwhile, Goodfellow is working to get prayer support for all of Iowa's 100,000 farmers.

THE TROUBLE WITH PRAYER

It is very difficult for researchers to prove that prayer really is responsible for improved physical and emotional heath. For one thing, when investigating faith in healing, it's difficult to maintain controlled studies. For example, in the Byrd Study, researchers had no way of knowing if people in the control group—those who were not being prayed for—actually had family members or friends praying for them.

For another, an accurate study, when repeated, should give the same results. (That's how you know the research is reliable.) But prayer doesn't always work that way. It is not 100 percent effective. We don't always get what we pray for.

How do you test how well something is working in a particular circumstance when it doesn't always work under any circumstance? And if it doesn't always work, should it be used at all? If someone—a clergyperson, relative, or physician—encourages a person with a deadly disease to pray for healing, is that someone guilty of pushing false hope on the patient?

Hope, Faith & Healing

"More than 130 controlled laboratory studies show, in general, that prayer or a prayerlike state of compassion, empathy, and love can bring about healthful changes in many types of living things, from humans to bacteria," Dossey writes in *Prayer Is Good Medicine*. "This does not mean prayer always works, any more than drugs and surgery always work but that, statistically speaking, prayer is effective."

Thus, from this point of view, the question is not, "Is it unethical to prescribe prayer?" but, "Is it unethical to fail to prescribe a treatment that has been shown, in many cases, to be effective?" Dossey, for one, decided that not praying for his patients "was the equivalent of withholding a needed medication or surgical procedure, and I began to pray for my patients daily."

WHAT PRAYER REALLY MEANS

The English word "prayer" comes from the Latin *precari*, which means to entreat, request earnestly, and plead. Based on these ancient roots, the *American Heritage Dictionary of the English Language, Third Edition*, defines prayer, first, as "a reverent petition made to God, a god, or another object of worship."

Indeed, petitionary prayer is a staple of all the world's religions. But prayer is sometimes defined by actions alone—by laying on of hands, for example. In his book *Prayer: Finding the Heart's True Home*, Richard J. Foster, a Quaker, writes, "The laying on of hands is used in Scripture in a number of ways such as the tribal blessing, the baptism of the Holy Spirit, and the impartation of spiritual gifts, but one of its most preeminent uses is in healing prayer. Jesus laid hands on the sick at Nazareth and healed them (Mark 6:5). He laid his hands on the blind man at Bethsaida twice before he fully recovered his sight (Mark 8:22–25). On the island of Malta the Apostle Paul laid hands on the sick, and they were healed (Acts 28:7–10)."

A study in the Netherlands in 1988 tested the effects of the laying on of hands. Three groups of patients with high blood pressure were studied. Once a week for 15 weeks, one group received laying on of hands administered by people trained in the technique. The second group received "healing thoughts" from people in another room. The third group was the control group, and received neither treatment.

Interestingly, the blood pressure of patients in all three groups decreased. The various treatments seemed to have no significant effect on physical health. But the patients who received the laying on of hands had a much greater sense of well-being than patients in the other two groups.

The many variations of prayer pose a host of questions for researchers. Is nonverbal prayer more effective than verbal prayer? Is prayer only effective when many people pray or are one individual's prayers enough to evoke a response? Only future investigations of prayer and healing can answer our many questions.

Simple Prayer

In *Prayer: Finding the Heart's True Home*, Richard J. Foster, a Quaker, explains the most basic form of prayer:

"In the same way that a small child cannot draw a bad picture, so a child of God cannot offer a bad prayer. So we are brought to the most basic, the most primary form of prayer: Simple Prayer. Let me describe it for you. In Simple Prayer we bring ourselves before God just as we are, warts and all. Like children before a loving father, we open our hearts and make our requests. We do not try to sort things out, the good from the bad. We simply and unpretentiously share our concerns and make our petitions. We tell God, for example, how frustrated we are with the coworkers at the office or the neighbor down the street. We ask for food, favorable weather, and good health."

WHEN PRAYER DOESN'T WORK

Research is beginning to confirm what people of faith have always known: Prayer can indeed work. But what about when it doesn't? Some say we must simply accept this as a mystery of faith. Yet it is human nature to want answers. Unanswered prayer is more a spiritual and theological problem than a scientific one. And it is a problem not just because we don't get what we ask for, but because the Scriptures—on which many people base their faith—do promise answers to prayer.

In the Hebrew Scriptures (Isaiah 38:1–5), the righteous king of Israel, Hezekiah, prayed for healing from a terminal disease and was granted an additional 15 years of life (see box below).

For Christians, the promises of answered prayer recorded in the New Testament are unequivocal. To cite one example, Jesus tells his disciples, "'Therefore I say to you, whatever things you ask when you pray, believe that you receive them, and you will have them.'" (Mark 11:24)

Perhaps effective prayer requires belief. Research has shown us that belief increases the effectiveness of any treatment. There is no reason why prayer should be any different.

Hezekiah's Healing

"In those days Hezekiah was sick and near death. And Isaiah the prophet, the son of Amoz, went to him and said to him, 'Thus says the Lord: "Set your house in order, for you shall die and not live."'

"Then Hezekiah turned his face toward the wall, and prayed to the Lord, and said, 'Remember now, O Lord, I pray, how I have walked before You in truth and with a loyal heart, and have done what is good in Your sight.' And Hezekiah wept bitterly.

"Then the word of the Lord came to Isaiah, saying, 'Go and say to Hezekiah, "Thus says the Lord, the God of David your father: 'I have heard your prayer, I have seen your tears; and I will add to your days 15 years.'"" (Isaiah 38:1–5)

Sometimes, healing prayer is offered, but healing does not come. In the book *Prayer: Finding the Heart's True Home*, Foster writes, "Under no circumstances are we to tell those receiving prayer that it is their fault: that they lack the faith, or that there must be some sin in them that is hindering the prayer, or any such thing. This will only redouble the burden they must carry. . . ." Blame is simply not the issue.

While suffering people always and understandably want an immediate end to their suffering, people of faith accept—sometimes wholeheartedly, sometimes with anguish—that God may have His reasons for allowing their suffering to continue. The Scriptures of many religions—as well as shelves of books in modern bookstores—are full of stories of men and women who endured great suffering, and, as a result, became extraordinarily strong and loving human beings who now inspire the rest of humanity to be the same way.

Thus, if God is all-knowing, it is wise to end our prayers with, "Thy will be done." Such a prayer is the essence of faith. "Using a 'Thy will be done' or 'May the best thing happen' approach in prayer requires faith and trust that the best outcome will prevail," writes Dossey in *Prayer Is Good Medicine*. "It also means setting aside our preferences and demands. This can be very difficult, because most of us feel we know in advance what's best, and we waste no time in telling the Absolute what to do."

Carter Morris, whose daughter Heyward is alive and well today because of a miraculous answer to prayer, has a special

Holy Words

The following words have come to be known as the *Prayer of an Unknown Confederate Soldier*. They are, perhaps, the most satisfactory answer to the problem of unanswered prayer.

I asked God for strength that I might achieve;
I was made weak that I might learn to obey.

I asked for health that I might do great things;
I was given infirmity, that I might do better things.

I asked for riches that I might be happy;
I was given poverty that I might be wise.

I asked for power that I might have the praise of men;
I was given weakness that I might feel the need of God.

I asked for all things that I might enjoy life;
I was given life that I might enjoy all things.

I got nothing that I had asked for,
but everything that I had hoped for.

Almost despite myself my unspoken prayers were answered;
I am, among all men, most richly blessed.

sensitivity to those whose prayers have not been answered. In *Expect a Miracle*, author Dan Wakefield quotes her: "You hear the word *miracle* a lot now. I don't use it lightly. So many people don't get one. When Heyward was still in a coma and we didn't know if she'd ever recover, people came and told us their miracles of a child recovering, and I felt like throwing something.

"We don't flaunt our miracle. What do you say to those people who don't have one, whose children will be in a hospital the rest of their life? We visit people now in rehab who may be there for years or permanently. It's not fair."

It's *not* fair. But it takes faith in God to believe that whatever happens is okay. People of faith believe that while God does not always show up and perform a miracle, God always shows up. And for most people, there is, after all, faith that death is not the end.

Religious Participation

Scientific research has also investigated another aspect of religious faith: participation in an organized religion or a faith community. The majority of religious Americans are Christians, so many Americans are members of church groups. But being religious can also mean being a member of a synagogue, temple, or other faith community.

It's important to keep in mind that not all people who are religious choose to be part of a faith community. The research findings of the 1990 Gallup poll found that, while 95% of Americans believe in God, only 42% regularly attend religious services. Why?

A Child's Thoughts on Unanswered Prayer

For his book *The Spiritual Life of Children*, Robert Coles talked with Christian, Jewish, and Muslim boys and girls about their religious beliefs.

In this excerpt, a 12-year-old Catholic girl named Meaghan is talking about her father's friend, a neighbor who is dying of cancer.

"He is the nicest person you'll ever meet. Our priest says he's a saint! He's ready to help everyone. Even now, he'll call people up if they're in trouble, and he'll give you the shirt off his back, my dad says. And he's dying! We can pray, but he'll die soon! My dad says it's just not fair—but you know, sure enough, it's not fair to us, but it could be fair to him! Maybe he'll be better off away from here—all the trouble. His son's bicycle was stolen, and he's had his radio in his car stolen, and because he told the kids to stop shouting at the colored kids, the blacks, he had a threat: A guy phoned him up and told him he'll 'get it.' My friend (the man's daughter) said her father never heard such bad words in his life. Maybe God heard them, too! Maybe He's up there, and He's sitting someplace, and He's saying: Francis Boyle is a good man, and he has suffered enough, and I'm going to call him right up here, and he can have a long, long rest, and no one will swear at him, and he won't have that cancer anymore, and it's very painful, and he's suffered enough."

Some Americans may be too ill to attend services. Some people believe in God but are not committed to any particular religion's ideas. Some individuals simply haven't found a faith community where they feel comfortable. And some can't find—or don't make—the time.

Of course, it's a personal—and sometimes difficult—decision to become part of a faith community. Becoming a member of a religious organization may not be such a bad idea, however. Research shows that people who attend churches, synagogues, and temples enjoy more health benefits than those who don't participate in services—in addition to the spiritual benefits that are gained from attendance.

One of the first studies of the relationship between church attendance and health was reported in the *Journal of Chronic Disorders* in 1972. The study looked at death rates among nearly 92,000 people in one county in Maryland. The group of people who went to church every week had fewer deaths than the group that went to services less frequently or not at all. Specifically, weekly churchgoers experienced 50% fewer deaths from coronary disease, 56% fewer deaths from the lung disease emphysema, 74% fewer deaths from the liver disease cirrhosis, and 53% fewer deaths from suicide than the non-churchgoers.

A nine-year study of death rates in Alameda County, California, reported similar results. Church members had lower death rates than people who were not members of a church. A later study of women in Tecumseh, Michigan, found that those who attended church lived longer.

And, as it turns out, going to church can do more than increase your life expectancy. A study at Wayne State University in Detroit found that African-American men who regularly attended religious services were less depressed, smoked fewer cigarettes, and drank less alcohol than their counterparts who didn't attend church services.

David Larson, M.D., president of the National Institute for Healthcare Research (NIHR), oversaw a study that tracked the blood pressure of 400 white men in rural Georgia for 30 years. The study results found that churchgoers had lower blood pressure levels than people who did not attend church services very frequently.

More recently, in 1996, Duke University psychiatrist Harold Koenig reported the results of a study by the National Institute on Aging. The study of 4,000 elderly people in North Carolina found that those who attended religious services were physically healthier and less depressed than those who didn't attend. Interestingly, the study found that being part of the "electronic church"—watching religious television—and praying alone did not have the same health benefits as being part of a religious community.

Some researchers think churchgoers are healthier because the faith community provides a strong network of social, emotional, and spiritual support. Feelings of being isolated, alone, and uncared for are unhealthy for anyone; any community or support group that prevents such feelings will help to enhance health. Other researchers suggest that participation in organized religion may be beneficial because, most often, the faith community is a place where many unhealthy behaviors are frowned upon.

In the Wayne State University study, the churchgoing men may have smoked less and drank less because smoking and drinking heavily are not acceptable behaviors in most churches. Thus, going to church may be an effective method of behavior modification that leads to good health and long life. (In the Seventh Day Adventist church, most Seventh Day Adventists are vegetarians, nondrinkers, and nonsmokers. Studies have consistently shown that Adventists tend to have longer life expectancies than the general population—nine years longer for men, four years longer for women—and much lower death rates from certain diseases.)

Matthews believes that the actual content of religious services can also have "measurable physiological effects." That is, congregational singing and praying actually may have a beneficial effect on physical health. According to Matthews, the religious service is a place to meet God, and a place where God meets the needs of many people in many ways.

FAITH AND THE FUTURE

Studies of the role of faith in healing are beginning to have an impact on the health care system.

In October 1996, Yankelovich Partners surveyed doctors attending a meeting of the American Academy of Family Practitioners. Of 296 doctors surveyed, 99% said they believed that religious faith could heal; 75% said they believed that prayer could help people get well. These figures are much higher than would be expected, given results of past surveys that asked health care professionals the same types of questions. Clearly, something is changing their minds.

Schools of medicine such as the highly respected Johns Hopkins University, Ohio State University, and Penn State University now offer a variety of courses and programs on spirituality and medicine. More universities are adding similar courses every year. Harvard Medical School has even established a biannual conference called Spirituality and Healing in Medicine.

Interestingly, it is not just the medical community, but also the religious community, that is responding to the research.

"The more we learn about faith's medical prowess, the more we see mainline religious denominations returning to the healing fold," writes Benson in *Timeless Healing*. He notes that Andover Newton Theological School, among others, has put faith healing into its curriculum, and quotes an official of the school as saying, "Healing was once a major part of the mission of the church but we abdicated it. We began to think that healing was a secular enterprise. But now, having become immersed in the study of mind/body connections, we realize we have a valuable role. We've become less self-conscious about it, that healing is part of the Christian tradition, that it isn't just a gimmick from a charlatan. Now faith healing is a central focus for us and we hope to be at the forefront in teaching others about it."

Francis McNutt, a former Dominican priest, was an early leader in bringing the church back to its healing roots. Mc-Nutt and his wife, Judith, now head Christian Healing Ministries, an organization that helps local churches begin their own healing ministries.

The Jewish community, too, is reclaiming its role in healing. Some temples now offer healing services; more and more Jewish congregations are interested in participating. Elat Chayyam, a Jewish "center for healing and renewal" in Woodstock, New York, holds a variety of healing workshops.

As both the medical and religious communities respond to early research, everyone agrees that more studies are needed. Researchers are calling for long-term studies that clarify the results of the healing effects of prayer. Matthews is now conducting a carefully structured study in which people trained by McNutt are offering patients spiritual counseling and both verbal and nonverbal prayer (laying on of hands).

FAITH AND THE HEALTH CARE SYSTEM

If you want faith to play a role in your health care, here are five ways to make it happen.

Be prepared: Talk to your family members and friends about their experiences with faith and healing. Take every opportunity to learn about people and treatments that embrace both faith and medicine. Begin looking for the right healers for you. By the way, the best time to begin looking for a doctor is when you're healthy—not when you're stressed with illness.

Be choosy: Choose a healer carefully. A warm, fuzzy personality, or a willingness to pray with you, isn't enough. You want a combination of good faith *and* good medicine. Ask people you know, especially those who share your faith, if they can recommend a doctor. Ask how that doctor brings faith into his medical practice. Choose a doctor who treats you like a person, not a disease.

Hope, Faith & Healing

In his book, *Peace, Love & Healing*, Bernie S. Siegel, M.D., writes, "Doctors who persist in thinking they can cure the disease without caring for the person may be excellent technicians, but they are incomplete doctors, because they have an incomplete understanding of illness." Treating you like a person means, at the very least, listening to you attentively and respectfully.

Try to choose a doctor whose commitment to the role of faith in healing matches your own. One good way to find out where the doctor stands is by discussing some of the studies you've read about. If the doctor responds enthusiastically and adds his or her own experiences with faith and healing, you've struck gold. If the doctor becomes uncomfortable or argumentative, interview other candidates. You have a right to express your beliefs and be treated with respect. And just as doctors should not be disrespectful of your beliefs, they also should not press their own beliefs on you.

Be realistic: Remember that even the best doctors have bad days. Understand, too, that the reunion of faith and medicine can be awkward, even for doctors who embrace it. In his book *A Physician's Witness to the Power of Shared Prayer*, William Haynes, M.D., of the Medical Center at Princeton, describes the gradual and difficult process through which he brought his faith into his medical practice. He began by telling patients at the time of their release from his care that he had been praying for them. He writes that "this took great courage on my part because of the unorthodoxy of prayer as an adjunct to the standard medical treatment. Just the thought of mentioning it was frightening." Next, Haynes began telling his hospitalized patients that he was praying for them. Only several months later did he begin asking patients if they would like him to pray with them. His offer of shared prayer, he reports, has never been turned down.

Realize your doctor may be waiting for you to make the first move. Some doctors say they listen for the language of faith in their patients' conversation, and respond accordingly. That way, they don't have to worry about pushing faith where it's not wanted. Your doctor has no way of knowing, at the outset, if you're a believer or a nonbeliever. So, don't be afraid to send your doctor a signal. Tell the doctor that you are praying for healing or that your friends and family are praying for you. It may be just the opening the doctor is looking for.

Be involved: Although it is perfectly reasonable to want your doctor to acknowledge your faith, it is not reasonable to expect him or her to be responsible for your spiritual well-being. That's your job. If you have an established spiritual life and are satisfied with it, great. If not, you are probably aware of areas you would like to strengthen.

Maybe you have faith, but aren't part of a faith community, such as a church or synagogue. Faith grows when it is shared. And, as the research shows, participation in a community of believers is one way to unleash the healing power of faith. It's not always easy to find your spiritual home, so don't be afraid to visit different groups. Ask questions and express your needs. And, by all means, pray for guidance!

Maybe you're just not comfortable participating in a religious group. Many people feel that they don't even know how to pray. Nearly everybody is intimidated by shared prayer at first. Ask a member of the clergy for encouragement, guidance, and good books about prayer. If you know someone who is very comfortable with prayer, ask that person to share what he or she has learned about it, and to pray with you.

If you see weaknesses in your own spiritual life, reach out for help in strengthening those areas. Spiritual wholeness is its own reward. Better health is just one of the fringe benefits.

Be yourself: If you want your doctor to treat you like a person, you have to let him or her get to know you as a person. Be open and honest, not only about your religious beliefs, but about your life and health. In *Peace, Love & Healing*, Siegel tells the story of a patient named Jake who had a brain tumor: "When the surgeon came down the hall Jake reached out to shake his hand but the surgeon pulled his hand back. Jake thought that the surgeon might be trying to protect his hands, so he then asked for a pat on the head instead. But the doctor again pulled back, saying that they were running late and needed to get to the O.R. At that point Jake roared, 'I refuse to have this man work on me! If he won't shake my hand or pat my head, I'm not letting him go into my brain!'" Siegel goes on to say that studies show that patients who ask a lot of questions and maintain their individuality have stronger immune systems and better survival rates than submissive patients.

But, you may not always be able to choose your doctor. In some cases, your insurance company may limit your choice or choose your physicians for you. You may be hospitalized and have to deal with a whole gang of medical scientists. At such times, it's easy to give up and give in, but if you have questions, ask them. If you're angry, say so. Pray, sing, and shout *hallelujah* should the occasion arise. Surround yourself with the support of fellow believers: friends, family, clergy, your faithful doctor.

And remember to be yourself, and keep the faith.

CHAPTER 2
Hope and Healing

In times of trouble, all we can do is hope for the best—which, as you shall see, is not such a bad idea. Research shows that hope actually can bring about happy endings. Hope is one part belief and one part attitude; it's a mixture of perseverance and surrender. And hope is always there for the ask-

ing—you don't have to be born with it, you don't have to pay for it, and you never have to run out of it. In other words, hope springs eternal.

Did you know hope can heal? Indeed, if you know how to use it, hope can be strong medicine.

HOW HOPE HELPS

At 24, Patricia Murphy was realizing her lifelong dream: She was on her way to medical school. She had graduated from college with a pre-med degree and was studying for the medical school entrance exams. One night, as she drove to her second-shift job in southern California, Murphy's car was rear-ended by a drunk driver. She suffered a head injury and severe whiplash. Two disks in her spine were ruptured and her left kneecap was smashed. Her ribs, nose, and jaw were broken as well as several bones in her right hand.

At the hospital, doctors placed Murphy in a drug-induced coma to help prevent brain damage. After three weeks, she stabilized. But, when she awoke from the coma, she didn't recognize her father. In fact, she remembered nothing about her life before the accident. Her speech was impaired. She couldn't even write.

In the days that followed, she drifted in and out of sleep. At one point, Murphy overheard a conversation outside her room. Her father was telling one of the doctors that she had been about to enter medical school at the time of the accident. "Well, she can forget about medical school," was the doctor's reply. Later, both a neurologist and a psychologist would tell Murphy the same thing.

In fact, doctors also told Murphy and her parents that she would never be able to take care of herself, hold a job, or become pregnant. "I refused to believe them," Murphy says. "I told them I was going to medical school." Murphy's biggest worry, however, was that the memory of her education wouldn't come back to her and she'd have to repeat all the pre-med classes.

"I was a bad patient. I didn't take anything the doctors told me at face value. I questioned everything," Murphy says.

Hope, Faith & Healing

For the next three years, Murphy suffered dizzy spells. For six years, as a result of the head injury, she suffered seizures. (At one point, her driver's license had to be revoked.) But, despite her physical limitations, Murphy participated in various forms of physical therapy, trying to recapture her life before the accident.

Over time, Murphy's speech returned to normal. When her seizures stopped, she insisted, against her doctors' advice, on gradually stopping her pain and seizure medications. She bought a house and moved into it alone—again, against her doctors' advice. She enrolled in pre-med classes and was relieved to discover that she remembered most of the material.

Late in 1996, nearly a decade after the accident, Patricia Murphy declared herself fully recovered. After all, she seemed to have defied the odds her doctors had given her. She was able to take care of herself. She was pregnant. And, on Christmas Eve, she received a letter informing her of her acceptance into medical school. She was thrilled, but not surprised. She had never hoped for anything less.

WHAT IS HOPE?

As long as men and women have faced the hardships of life, there has been hope. And like faith, hope's ability to heal has caught the attention of the medical world. In fact, research shows that hope can help people survive all types of challenges—including terminal diseases.

HOPE IS A BELIEF

Hope is a belief that things will go your way. When they don't, hope tells you life will get better. And, with hope, things aren't as bad as they seem: There are always possibilities, options, and alternatives. Hope is desire and the belief that your desires will be fulfilled. But hope is always seasoned with uncertainty. We hope for what we cannot know for sure.

HOPE IS A FEELING

Hope is an emotion. How hope feels depends on how much uncertainty is mixed in with it. Strong, confident hope makes us feel lighthearted and excited. Desperate hope can cause a pounding heart and a feeling of uneasiness. These emotional qualities of hope may be largely responsible for hope's powerful impact on the body.

HOPE IS AN ATTITUDE

The kind of hope that heals is a strong and willful hope. Several years ago, the British medical journal *The Lancet* reported a study of 57 women who had breast cancer. The study found that the women who responded to their cancer with a "fighting spirit" were more likely to be alive and cancer-free five years after their diagnosis than women who accepted the diagnosis stoically. (In fact, acceptance of the disease was actually found to be a sign of hopelessness.) Ten years after the women were diagnosed, 70 percent of the "fighters" were still living, compared to 20 percent of the patients who were re-signed to their illness.

To understand the assertive side of hope, it's important to understand the difference between denial and defiance. Denial is the first of several stages that many patients go through after they are diagnosed with a serious illness. And, while most patients go through this stage, a few get stuck there. A patient trapped in denial cannot commit to needed treatments and life

changes. What's more, denial suffocates inner resources like hope that can help fight disease.

But defiance is different. Denial says, "I'm not sick." Defiance says, "I'm sick, but I'm not going to let this thing ruin my life. I'm going to fight it, and I plan to win." That's the kind of hope that heals.

You have the right to defy the odds your doctor gives you, to choose a different treatment than he or she recommends, and to manage your illness and your life in the way that best suits you. But you cannot defy God. In *Peace, Love & Healing*, author Bernie S. Siegel, M.D., writes, "...you have to know what to fight for and what to leave to God. Your rights and your individuality are things you owe it to yourself to fight for, by saying that you will not be a doormat, by insisting that your doctor treat you with respect, by making sure you get answers to your questions, by wearing your own clothes in the hospital, by participating in decisions that need to be made about your treatment. But there are other times when you must have faith and trust, when you must allow God to handle the burden so that you can be at peace. This combination of a fighting spirit and a spiritual faith is the best survival mechanism I know."

HOPE IS IN THE PAST, PRESENT, AND FUTURE

Mostly, we think of hope as being about the future, and, mostly, it is. But hope also lives in the present and reaches into our past. Hope uses light from the past to brighten present darkness and illuminate the future. "Remembered wellness," a term coined by Herbert Benson, M.D., author of *Timeless Healing*, refers to the practice of remembering times of health and happiness to help our bodies recapture and recreate that health. Hope is an important part of remembered wellness. Hope assures us that what once was can be again.

HOPE IS DETERMINED

Hope perseveres. Hope doesn't give up after one disappointment, or two setbacks, or three failures. In fact, hope may be so bold that, even if it fails at something small, it will try again for something even bigger.

For example, once there was a man who hoped to have his own business, but twice he failed. At the age of 27, he had a nervous breakdown. Later, when he hoped to become an elected official, he ran for office eight times, and eight times he lost. At the age of 51, Abraham Lincoln finally achieved something he had hoped for. He was elected president of the United States.

Hope Is a Coping Mechanism

Hope, in one form or another, weaves in and out of our lives. We hope it won't rain over the holiday. We hope to get a huge raise or maybe even win the lottery. We hope the test results come back negative—or, in some cases, positive. The higher the stakes, the more intensely we hope, and the more aware we are of hoping.

In a 1995 article in *Cancer Nursing*, Tone Rustøen, a registered nurse in Oslo, Norway, writes, "Hope is not normally present in a person's consciousness. It reaches consciousness when one is faced with a crisis or a conflict, like getting a cancer diagnosis."

Hope is an effective way to cope with all types of serious illnesses as well as other kinds of suffering, such as grief. Hope prepares the mind and body to endure suffering. Hope reminds us that this, too, shall pass.

Hope stirs us to action; it gives us the energy and the will to bring about what we want. Writes Rustøen in *Cancer Nursing*, "Hope functions as a foundation for dealing with life and guides one's actions. Strong hope gives strength and courage to press forward in handling difficult situations." Hope can make all our efforts worthwhile.

In the March/April 1993 issue of *Journal of ET Nursing*, Debra Broadwell-Jackson, R.N., Ph.D., writes that "the person who gains hope is committed to action if action is possible." After all, who would endure chemo-therapy, with all its ugly side effects, without the hope that out of the suffering will come healing? Who would per-severe through months of painful physical therapy without hope that through the pain, function will be restored?

A wish is an idle thing; a hope is a wish with wings.

HOPE IS FULL OF POSSIBILITIES

Of course, because no one knows the future, no one knows what is truly possible. "Hope that seems to be unrealistic, in terms of the professional's knowledge of a patient's prognosis, may appear realistic to a patient in terms of how he or she feels," writes Karen Wilkinson, R.N., in the July 1996 issue of *Professional Nurse*. "What is reality to a professional may have no meaning to a patient." Hope is what a person believes to be possible, despite the opinions of others.

HOPE IS FLEXIBLE

Hope changes its focus as personal beliefs and circumstances change. All human beings must die; to hope for life is not always reasonable. Thus, your focus may shift—you may hope for the best possible quality of life in the time that remains, the healing of any broken relationships, or a death that inspires others to live more fully. There is always a place for hope.

HOPE IS A GROUP PROJECT

When it comes to hope, no man or woman is really alone. Doctors, nurses, therapists, family, and friends all affect a person's hopefulness. In an article that appeared in the July 1996 issue of *Professional Nurse*, Wilkinson quotes a patient as saying, "Other people influence my hope by their willingness to share a part of themselves through their affirmation, reassuring presence, encouragement, willingness to listen attentively, to touch, and to share hopes and feelings."

Doctors in particular can have an especially strong impact on a patient's hope. Because we see our doctors as experts,

A Few Words About Hope

Hope is a risk that must be run. —*Georges Bernanos*

There are no hopeless situations; there are only men who have grown hopeless about them. —*Clare Boothe Luce*

At first we hope too much; later on, not enough. —*Joseph Roux*

We should not let our fears hold us back from pursuing our hopes.
—*John F. Kennedy*

If it were not for hopes, the heart would break. —*Thomas Fuller, MD*

It is hope that maintains most of humankind. —*Sophocles*

Hope is a strange invention—
A Patent of the Heart—
In unremitting action
Yet never wearing out. —*Emily Dickinson*

Hope is the best possession. None are completely wretched but those who are without hope, and few are reduced so low as that.
—*William Hazlitt*

Hope has as many lives as a cat or a king. —*Henry Wadsworth Longfellow*

Hope is brightest when it dawns from fears. —*Sir Walter Scott*

The miserable have no other medicine, but only hope.
—*William Shakespeare*

we are usually inclined to believe what they say. Hippocrates, the ancient Greek physician, understood this influence that doctors have on their patients. "Some patients," he wrote, "though conscious that their condition is perilous, recover their health simply through their contentment with the goodness of the physician."

Unfortunately, some patients die because their doctors suggest they will. So, if ever a doctor hands you a death sentence, get a second opinion. In *Head First: The Biology of Hope*, writer Norman Cousins relates the story of a woman who went to her doctor with an unexplained cough. The doctor ran some tests and told the woman that she had terminal cancer—and about 60 days to live. Although the woman had been working and living a normal life, upon hearing the diagnosis, she immediately stopped eating and lost 18 pounds in just over a week.

Fortunately, the woman pursued a second opinion. This doctor had a very different outlook. He told her that some people survived terminal diseases; he even introduced her to one person who had recovered from a disease similar to her own. The doctor recommended that she get the best possible medical treatment and use all of her inner resources—physical, emotional, and spiritual—to help her body heal. At the time when Cousins' book was published in 1989—long after the woman's 60-day death sentence—she still had cancer, but with hope, she was maintaining a good quality of life.

Too often, doctors are not aware of the impact of their words on their patients. What they say can often destroy any feelings of hope their patients may have. As an example, Louise Niessen, R.N., tells this story of her mother's death from breast cancer in the June 1995 issue of *The Canadian Nurse*. "My mother's method was to hold on to hope. Her relative peace of mind, however, was threatened more and more with each follow-up visit to the clinic. Her decline was reinforced by what we perceived as cold and detached professionals, slowly chipping away at hope. Subliminal messages have negative results.

"When the cancer clinic could offer no further treatment for my mother, we were seen by a student doctor we'd never met. He told us that we could expect another month, and that he was sorry if this was bad news. Our personal feelings of grief and disappointment were ignored."

From this painful personal experience, Niessen concluded that the doctors were wrong in giving her mother's life a deadline. It was that deadline that hurt her mother's hope more than anything else.

Siegel wholeheartedly agrees. In *Peace, Love & Healing,* he writes, "Perhaps more powerful than any visualization or other specific technique you can use to alter the inner environment of your body are feelings of hope and love. I consider it my job as a doctor to give my patients both, because that's what they need to be able to live. Since I don't know what the outcome will be for any individual, no matter what the pathology report says, I can in all honesty give everyone hope."

No doctor knows when a patient is going to die, or how fully a patient is going to recover. A doctor knows what the probabilities are, but they are just that: probabilities, not certainties. Doctors know something about what a disease will do to a person. What they don't know is what a person may do to a disease.

Considering the doctor's dilemma of communicating a diagnosis, is it possible to inform a patient truthfully about a serious diagnosis and still leave the patient with something to hold on to in the form of sustaining hope?

Writes Cousins in *Head First: The Biology of Hope,* "I have been with cancer patients at the time of diagnosis. I recall one circumstance in particular. I listened to a physician as he told the truth. He put it in the form of a challenge rather than a death sentence. He was not telling less than he knew; neither was he telling more than he knew. In his medical journals he had read of hundreds of unexpected remissions. And so he didn't feel under any obligation to provide any terminal date nor would he have done so even if asked. He was wise enough to know that some people confound all the predictions, and he didn't want to do anything or say anything that would have the effect of a hex on the patient."

Karl Menninger, M.D., the psychiatrist who cofounded the famous Menninger Clinic, declared in *The Vital Balance,* "It is our duty as physicians to estimate probabilities and to discipline expectations; but leading away from probabilities there are paths of possibility, towards which it is also our duty to hold aloft the light, and the name of that light is hope."

It is a doctor's duty to offer hope, whether or not the doctor agrees with the treatment the patient chooses. In *Peace, Love*

& *Healing*, Siegel writes of a woman who, when given a diagnosis of brain cancer and a 90-day death sentence, chose to go to Mexico for a nontraditional treatment that involves the ingestion of a substance derived from raw bitter almonds and apricot pits, called *laetrile*. A year later the woman felt quite well and was going on with her life, when she happened to run into the doctor who had given her the death sentence. He, of course, was shocked to see the woman alive and in such good health. When she told him laetrile had given her a new lease on life, the doctor forcefully told her that laetrile didn't work and that he could prove it to her. He didn't need to. The woman was convinced he was right—and she died that night.

"If the power of belief has enabled something to work for someone," Siegel writes, "I'm not about to use the authority of my profession to destroy its benefits. I know that hope and faith can sometimes provide patients with options that extend their lives when conventional medicine can do nothing."

And it's not just doctors who have a responsibility to safeguard hope. The attitudes and words of anyone a patient has contact with can have a strong impact on the patient's hope. Parents must take care that they speak hope, not fear and despair, to their sick children. Family members and friends of a person who is ill can either add to, or subtract from, the person's store of life-giving hope. People can keep hope alive for an individual who is too sick to hope.

On February 22, 1996, Alfredo Perez was teaching his elementary class at a Los Angeles school when shooting began outside. One bullet crashed through a window and hit Perez in the head. Doctors told Perez's wife, Virginia, that his chance of survival was zero percent. When Perez survived the initial trauma but remained unconscious for two months, doctors told his wife not to hope for more.

Exactly one year later, Perez and his wife appeared together at a news conference. Perez walked into the crowded room, followed closely by his wife, and spoke clearly and movingly  of his recovery so far—and the rebuilding he still had to do. Virginia Perez expressed her gratitude, saying that he couldn't have done as well without the doctors, nurses, physical therapists, and others. And she credited her husband for his determination, saying, "He never gave up."

But, behind the scenes of the news conference, nurses told reporters that Virginia Perez had been at her husband's side every day for the past year, encouraging him to keep striving for 100 percent recovery. Perhaps it was she who brought him back to health—by giving him all the hope he needed.

Hope, Faith & Healing

Hope Is Never "False"

The Perezes' experience is proof positive that there is no such thing as false hope. After watching doctors destroy her mother's hope, Niessen vowed to change the way she, as a nurse, relates to patients. "I will continue to listen to patients, as venting is a vital part of dealing with stress and anxiety," she wrote in *The Canadian Nurse*. "In addition, though, I now offer the positive encouragement I was afraid to offer before. Hope is never wrong."

Where there's life, there's hope. And as long as a person is alive, he or she has a right to hope.

Hope Is a Choice

Although hope is influenced by our environment and the people around us, ultimately, hope is an individual choice. You can't force a person who has chosen hopelessness to suddenly become hopeful. We can give hope only to those who are willing to receive it.

HOW HOPE HEALS

There is a word for the science of studying the links between emotional patterns and illness. Fortunately, this word, psychoneuroimmunology, can be abbreviated to PNI. PNI is a combination of psychology, neurophysiology, endocrinology, and immunology. Together, these sciences are showing us how hope and other emotions have the ability to heal.

So, how do emotions get translated into physical realities, and vice versa? Research suggests that both external events and internal events (thoughts and memories) seem to trigger certain patterns of chemical activity in the brain. Those chemicals send messages throughout the body—messages that profoundly affect what the body does.

The chemicals that carry messages from our minds to our bodies are called *peptides*. Peptides are molecules that are manufactured not only in our brains, but also in our immune systems. Scientists have identified about 60 different peptide molecules. You have probably heard of some of them, including endorphins and interferons.

Peptides are thought to be responsible for the placebo effect. Here's how it works, according to the peptide theory: A person takes a placebo medication—say, a sugar pill—with the belief that the pill will relieve pain. That positive belief causes the body to produce endorphins, which, in turn, relieve the pain. The placebo works, not because of any substance contained in the placebo, but because of substances the body produced in response to a belief about the placebo.

Is it possible to skip the sugar pill but still create hope that will jump-start the body's healing molecules? Research hasn't yet answered that question. So far, most studies on hope have focused on defining and measuring hope, rather than on studying hope's effect on health. But researchers have studied other states of mind and their effects on healing.

In the 1940s, Caroline Bedell Thomas, M.D., began a long-term study of the link between psychological characteristics and physical health. Thomas tracked 1,300 medical students who graduated from Johns Hopkins Medical School for the next 30 years. She found that people who had unhappy childhoods and kept their emotions bottled up inside were much more likely than others to get diseases like heart disease and cancer, and were also much more likely to suffer from depressive disorders and to commit suicide.

Also in the 1940s, a long-term study began of more than 200 male students at Harvard University. The study, which tracked the men for 40 years, investigated the relationship between their mental and physical health. About 35 years into the study (when the subjects were in their early 50s), the researchers looked at the physical health of the men with the best and worst mental health. Of the 48 men with the worst mental health, 18 either had serious chronic diseases or were deceased. Of the 59 men with the best mental health, only two were seriously ill or deceased.

Researchers Suzanne Kobasa, Ph.D., and Salvatore Maddi, Ph.D., at the University of Chicago studied executives who were under a lot of stress at work. During the study, approximately half of the executives got sick; the other half stayed healthy. The researchers found that the executives who stayed healthy tended to feel that they had some measure of control over their lives. They were also committed to choices they had made in their lives and generally found stress to be a challenge rather than a threat.

At the University of California, George F. Solomon, M.D., and Lydia Temoshok, M.D., have studied personality's link to disease in both AIDS and cancer patients. In cancer patients, they found that traits such as compliance, conformity, self-sacrifice, denial of anger, and repression of emotion made a person less likely to do well. In their research on AIDS patients, they found that people who have a sense of purpose, who take responsibility for their health, who express their emotions, and who have a sense of humor are likely to live longer than other people with AIDS who do not share these traits.

Psychologist Martin Seligman, Ph.D., of the University of Pennsylvania coined the term "explanatory style" to refer to a person's mental and emotional response to stress and illness. Explanatory style is how a person explains the events of his or her life. And while we cannot choose what happens to us, we can choose how we explain it to ourselves. Seligman studied the explanatory styles of 172 college students and was then able to predict which students would be sick a month later and a year later.

Hope, Faith & Healing

For example, a person who had an abusive childhood may say to himself, "My parents abused me because I am a bad person. I'll never accomplish anything worthwhile." That person's explanatory style leaves no room for hope. Another person with the same background might explain the abuse in a different way, such as, "My parents were abused by their parents; they were repeating the bad behavior they learned. It had nothing to do with me." That explanatory style makes it possible to break the abuse pattern and live a healthy, productive life.

In 1987, researchers summed up the results of the 40-year Harvard University study by claiming that a man's explanatory style at age 25 could predict what his health would be like at age 65. They also found that the health of pessimists began to decline sharply at about age 45.

Writing in the March/April 1993 issue of the *Journal of ET Nursing*, Debra Broadwell-Jackson, Ph.D., R.N., gives an example of how hope can turn a life around. As a wound-care specialist, she was asked to see a police officer who was suffering from several problems, including a wound that would not heal and malnutrition. The man was afraid he would not get well and therefore would never again be able to support his family. Because of his fears and his frustration with not healing, the man was hostile to the hospital staff. He complained constantly, refused to eat, and said he was hopeless.

Broadwell-Jackson convened a meeting of the man's family and all the hospital staff who were caring for him. At the meeting, she mapped out a strategy for helping the man find hope. Instead of trying to get him to stop complaining, she told everyone to encourage him to express his feelings. (Complaining was, after all, a natural reaction.) She also wanted the man to be as involved in his care as possible, so he could feel that he had some control over his health. Last, but not least, she told everyone to tell the man that he was doing better—making use of the placebo effect.

Soon this man's caregivers began to see signs of hope. He began to ask questions about his future. He gave the staff pointers on how to best dress his wounds. Finally, he began to smile and the comments he made to those around him changed from negative to positive.

As the man's mindset and personality improved, so did his physical condition. Slowly, his wounds healed. Eventually, the man was well enough to leave the hospital.

Broadwell-Jackson finishes the story: "Recently I had a surprise visit from the patient. He had gained weight and was planning on returning to work the next week. He hugged me and thanked me for not giving up on him. He told me that I gave him hope, and that hope was what gave him the energy to hang in there."

Unfortunately, hope, alone, is not enough to prevent or to cure serious illness. Genes and environment, as well as emotions and explanatory style, play a part in determining who will get sick, how they will get sick, and how they will re-

Hope Is Not Just for the Sick

Hope is important not only for people who are ill, but also for those individuals who care for the sick. Caregiving is a demanding job that takes enormous amounts of physical and emotional energy. Especially if the caregiver is very close to the person who is ill, being helpful can be as stressful as being sick.

Here are some ways that caregivers can maintain their own sense of hope.

1. Maintain relationships in which you are nurtured. In your role as a caregiver, you are just that: a giver. Balance that relationship with other relationships in your life in which you are the receiver of other people's time, energy, and care.

2. Have reasonable expectations. Be reasonable in terms of what you expect to be able to do for the person you are caring for. You can't make him or her well. Some days, you won't even be able to make the person feel better. All you can do is be there. That's good enough.

3. Take comfort and strength from your spiritual beliefs.

4. Take care of yourself physically and emotionally. Accept your limits. Get the rest you need. Eat well. Take time for a walk or other physical exercise, and do it alone or with someone whose company uplifts you. Rent a video that makes you laugh. Curl up on the couch and read a good book. Share memories with a friend. Collect hugs.

cover. But hope is one important factor that we can control. While we are born with our genes and often, to a large extent, are stuck with our environment, how we choose to use hope ultimately remains up to us.

SOURCES OF HOPE

Hope is something we all need. And hope is healing. So where do we find the hope that helps us live, thrive, and heal?

Where people find hope depends in part on where they are in their lives. In one study of young people, when asked what it was that gave them hope, they most often mentioned their successes and achievements, and a sense of control over their lives. These factors gave them hope for continued success and lifelong achievement.

The most common sources of hope for elderly people, according to several studies, are good physical and mental health, strong social support from family and/or friends, and religious faith. These factors give older people hope that they will be able to cope successfully with the challenges of aging.

Researchers have identified the following sources of hope among people facing health problems:

HUMAN RELATIONSHIPS

Doctors, counselors, and clergy often speak of a person's need for a strong, supportive family—especially when illness strikes. But, as we have seen, relationships with friends and health care

You Mustn't Quit

—author unknown

When things go wrong, as they sometimes will,
When the road you're trudging seems all uphill,

When the funds are low and the debts are high
And you want to smile, but you have to sigh,

When care is pressing you down a bit,
Rest! if you must—but never quit.

Life is queer, with its twists and turns,
As every one of us sometimes learns,

And many a failure turns about
When he might have won if he'd stuck it out;

Stick to your task, though the pace seems slow—
You may succeed with one more blow.

Success is failure turned inside out—
The silver tint of the clouds of doubt—

And you never can tell how close you are,
It may be near when it seems afar;

So stick to the fight when you're hardest hit—
It's when things seem worst that you mustn't quit.

Hope, Faith & Healing

professionals are also important sources of hope.

To many people, a strong family can remedy feelings of hopelessness. But many people simply don't have supportive families. What's important is having people in your life you care about—and who obviously care about you. It doesn't matter if these are  people you meet at work, on the bus, in your neighborhood, at church, or even in line at the grocery store. And it doesn't matter if you have ten friends or just two—a little love can go a long way.

RELIGIOUS FAITH OR SPIRITUAL BELIEFS

Stephen G. Post, Ph.D., associate director of the Center for Biomedical Ethics at Case Western Reserve University, makes the connection between faith and hope, writing in an issue of *Mind/Body Medicine* (Vol. 2, No. 1, 1997): "Hope is the subjective sense of having a worthwhile future in the midst of anxiety. It is inherently relational, and is usually mediated through religious ideation, symbol, practice, and community." People who have faith in a higher power have somewhere to turn in times of need.

A Sense of Purpose

Knowing that our lives serve a purpose is a source of hope that strengthens our will to live. People want to survive when they have a sense of purpose, whether it's to "take care of the kids" or "watch their grandchildren grow." Some people claim to survive illness or accident because it

"just wasn't their time." A person with a purpose not only hopes, but expects, to be able to achieve his goals.

Reachable Goals

When you set a goal, you create a sense of hope. When you reach that goal, you hope to achieve new ones. This kind of hope can be a powerful ally in healing. Imagine a cancer patient who reaches her goal of being able to stay at the job she loves for one more month. When she attains that goal, she may be energized and encouraged enough to stay at work for another month, and another. Remember the following Chinese proverb: A journey of a thousand miles begins with a single step.

A Sense of Self-Worth

Having a strong sense of self-worth simply means that the faith you have in yourself is unshakable. When you feel sick and look sick, a solid sense of worth can provide a source of hope that, as before, you will be well again.

A Sense of Humor

Laughter and a lighthearted spirit are sources of hope. Laughter makes people feel better, both emotionally and physically. A good laugh can make us forget our troubles for a moment or put them in perspective. When we laugh, we remember that there's more to life than our pain, our disease, or our prognosis. Humor and laughter bring hope into the present by making us feel better even in the midst of suffering. And it can help us forget our fear.

Happy Memories

People who have been sick for a long time sometimes forget what it was like to be well. They see themselves only as sick. Ultimately, their whole lives—their thoughts, activities, and goals—revolve around their illness. As time goes by, they forget to hope for a healthier future.

Happy memories are a very effective antidote to hopelessness. Positive memories allow people to remember what it was like to be healthy, which sparks hope that they can be healthy again.

Personal Attributes

Characteristics you like about yourself can be an important source of hope. A person who knows she is courageous, resourceful, buoyant, and able to endure suffering can be confident that each of these traits will be helpful in fighting illness.

PERSONAL ENVIRONMENT

To find out what hope means to different people, one study asked 12 people over the age of 65 to take photographs of things that gave them hope. Each of the 12 people took 12 photographs over a one-week period.

Some of the photographs showed symbols and images of well-known, nearly universal sources of hope, such as churches and family members. But some of the pictures showed more individual choices. One person took a photo of a mailbox, where she always hoped to find a card or letter from someone special. Another person took a picture of the kitchen table, a source of familiarity and comfort. Similarly, one person took a picture of a favorite room at home, a room that gave a sense of well-being. One person took a picture of a clown, who gave hope for laughter and joy.

This study focused on an often-overlooked source of hope: our environment. Think of how you feel after watching a movie with a violent or tragic story line compared to how you feel after watching a good comedy or an inspiring story. The movies and television shows we watch, the books we read, the music we listen to, and all the other sights, sounds, and objects that make up our environment can build or destroy hope.

Hope, Faith & Healing

In the New Testament's Book of Philippians, Paul wrote, "...whatever things are true, whatever things are noble, whatever things are just, whatever things are pure, whatever things are lovely, whatever things are of good report, meditate on these things." (Philippians 4:8) This is still good advice.

NATURE

Suffering never seems natural to us. When suffering suddenly occurs, we feel that life has suddenly gone horribly wrong. But nature can offer us not only hope, but a promise, that everything is going according to a plan, and that neither suffering nor pleasure lasts forever.

Just imagine that you had grown to adulthood in the tropics and had never heard of winter, much less seen it. Then imagine that, for some reason, you migrated far north. Before many months went by, it would seem as if the whole world was dying around you. Leaves would drop, animals would slowly disappear, summer's sounds would cease, and even the sun would seem to lose its life. You would be convinced that the world was at an end, and that you, too, would soon die. As the world continued to grow colder and darker, you would begin to lose hope.

But then, one day, you would notice a blade of green rising from the soil or a new bud forming on the seemingly dead limb of a tree. Spring cannot be stopped any more than winter can. The sun will rise as surely as it sets. Therein lies hope.

EDUCATION

Education provides a source of hope as well. Researchers have found that the more educated people are, the more hopeful they tend to be. Education offers hope by giving

people a broader view of life, a sense that there are always options and alternatives. Education also may give a person a greater sense of purpose as well as confidence in his or her own abilities to successfully cope with pain and illness.

FINANCIAL WELL-BEING

Can money bring us hope? Financial resources can provide a sick person with better access to the very best medical professionals and treatments. Money can give a person the freedom to pursue different avenues of healing, to explore every possibility for a cure. Perhaps, most importantly, being financially secure means avoiding the constant worry of not being able to cover your health care costs.

AVAILABILITY OF MEDICAL CARE

Most people in the world can't take the availability of medical care for granted. In some parts of the world, for example,

Hope, Faith & Healing

cataracts are a sentence to blindness because the surgery to remove them is not available.

But a person living in the United States who is diagnosed with cataracts can turn to modern medicine as a source of hope. Those individuals with more challenging health problems—even those to whom medicine cannot guarantee a cure—can take hope from the simple fact that they have access to some of the best medical care the world has ever known.

There are countless other sources of hope. Only you know what gives you hope. Remember, anything that offers hope has the potential to heal.

THREATS TO HOPE

Researchers have identified three factors that destroy hope. Because these factors are common "side effects" of serious illness, it is important to know what they are and what to do to prevent or reverse them.

ISOLATION

Isolation is a frequent side effect of long-term illness because the person who is ill is often hospitalized and separated from family, friends, coworkers, and normal routines. People who are too ill to go on with life may be painfully aware that life is going on without them. To make matters worse, it is not uncommon for friends and family to avoid the patient. Sometimes people do this because of their own fears of illness and death. Some people stay away from sick people because they don't know what to say, are afraid of saying the wrong thing, or are afraid of being unable to control their own emotions.

Battling a serious illness is, unavoidably, a lonely struggle. The sick person, alone, suffers the pains of the illness, the side effects of the treatment, the life-and-death uncertainty. But to  keep hope alive, family, friends, and health care professionals must do what they can to minimize these feelings of loneliness. If a friend or family member is hospitalized, make sure to visit the patient often. Talk about how much the sick person is missed at home, work, church, or school. If the patient is well enough, plan short outings from the hospital. If the patient can't leave the hospital, don't forget to bring holiday, birthday, and other celebrations to the patient.

LOSS OF IDENTITY

Very sick people are usually unable to fulfill the roles that they typically play: Mothers can't mother, fathers can't father, students can't study, nurses can't nurse, and firefighters can't fight fires. The hospital routine can add to feelings of inadequacy and insignificance when patients are shuffled from one doctor to another, called by the wrong name, matched with the wrong chart, and clad in look-alike hospital gowns. In such an environment, it takes a strong personality to hold onto one's individuality. But even individuals with strong personalities may not feel up to the task when they're ill.

To help maintain your sense of identity during hospitalization, in *Peace, Love & Healing*, Siegel recommends that patients insist on wearing their own clothes in the hospital. He also suggests decorating the hospital room to make it more comfortable. Do whatever it takes to remind yourself—and everyone around you—that you are an important human being who deserves to be treated with respect and dignity.

PAIN THAT IS NOT CONTROLLED

Uncontrolled, ongoing pain is devastating. Chronic pain can lead to sleeplessness, inability to think clearly or perform routine tasks, irritability, and depression. Some people even try to escape from the pain by turning to alcohol and drugs. The physical and mental toll of chronic pain can quickly destroy hope.

The problem with pain is that it can be difficult to treat. Sometimes doctors are unable to pinpoint the cause of the pain. Also, pain is subjective; only the person suffering it can assess how truly bad it is.

When dealing with chronic pain, it's important to have a doctor who understands how devastating the pain is. The physician should be committed to relieving the pain. If standard treatments aren't successful, the physician should be willing to try alternative approaches to pain relief. People suffering from debilitating chronic pain may need an advocate to keep them up-to-date with the various treatment options.

HOPELESSNESS

The flip side of hope is hopelessness, and it is as hurtful as hope is helpful. The North American Nursing Diagnosis Association defines hopelessness as "the subjective state in which an individual feels that alternatives and personal choices are limited or nonexistent, resulting in an inability to mobilize energy." Studies have shown that hopelessness can make people sick—and keep them from getting well.

In the 1950s, researchers at the University of Rochester identified three elements that resulted in what they called "the giving up—given up complex." The elements were hopelessness and helplessness, a poor self-image, and a lack of satisfaction from relationships and roles (such as being a parent, worker, volunteer, etc.). The researchers studied people with all kinds of serious illnesses and found that 70 to 80 percent of the patients had fallen into the giving up—given up complex *before* they became ill.

Hopelessness can make you sick. Are you feeling hopeless? Watch for these warning signs:

• Apathy and indifference; not caring about anything
• Passivity; accepting bad news, verbal abuse, and/or mistreatment without any protest

- Lack of emotions and feelings; emotional numbness
- Speaking of being despondent
- Withdrawal from relationships and activities
- Decreased appetite
- Increased sleep

We all have events in our lives that can trigger hope-lessness. As Seligman and other researchers have shown, it's not the event, but our response to it, that determines our health and our future. Any sign of hopelessness should be a warning that we're sending our bodies the wrong signals.

We are all capable of creating as much hope as we need. Here's how to make sure you will always have more than your fair share:

1. *Take a hope inventory.* Do some research on yourself. Are you hopeful or hopeless? Even if you think of yourself as a hopeful person, you may be surprised to find that some aspects of your life make you feel hopeless.

Help for the Hopeless

If a person is truly determined to drown in hopelessness, there really is nothing anyone can do about it. But, for most people, hopelessness is only a temporary crisis. Most people can be—and want to be—encouraged to hope again. Here are some ways to help a hopeless person:

Just listen. People who are hurting need to vent their frustrations and fears. Don't judge them and don't argue. Don't say things like, "You shouldn't talk like that." Let the person express feelings without interrupting them.

Sometimes, listening is all you'll need to do. But there are times when more may be asked of you. You can acknowledge hopelessness without agreeing with dire conclusions. A good response to forlorn feelings is, "It's understandable that you feel that way, but things really aren't as bad as they seem."

Put the person back in touch with her sources of hope. If she is religious, remind her of the comfort and strength to be found in her faith. Remind her of times past when fear and despair overwhelmed her, and were conquered; when it seemed that there was no way out and an open door appeared. Talk about the future and about people who love her. Hopelessness can build walls around people, trapping them in dark, empty cells. The key to hope is to release them from their cells into the world of light and possibilities.

Monitor your thoughts, words, and feelings. Do you usually feel happy and expectant or fearful and anxious? Are you full of hope about some things and hopeless about others? Discover what it is you can do to bring hope to those areas in your life where hope is lacking.

2. *Find the hope experts.* Everybody knows some hope experts. They're usually not too hard to find. They're the people who know how to keep hope alive—despite life's ups and downs. Hope experts are those people who seem to have perfect, easy lives and not a care in the world. But get to know some of these people and you're likely to find that they have their fair share of troubles—sometimes more. The spring in their steps and the sparkle in their eyes come from a hopeful outlook, not from perfect circumstances.

3. *Appoint a hope committee.* As we've seen, the people in our lives can make or break our hope. It's important to surround yourself with people who give you hope. Make a list of all the people you know whose words and actions lift your spirits and plan to spend more time with them. And, of course, make sure you return the favor and bring hope into their lives as well.

4. *Be prepared to deal with hope snatchers.* In every universe, there are black holes. Just as we all know hope experts, we are also all acquainted with those who specialize in hopelessness. When in their company, try to explain to them that hopelessness is bad for their health—and yours. Kindly, but

firmly, inform them that, when you're around, they'll have to keep their hopeless views to themselves. In the meanwhile, keep shining your light of hope in their direction—maybe some of it will rub off.

5. *Know where your hope is.* Figure out what it is in life that brings you hope. Is it strong relationships? Music? Fulfilling obligations or goals? When you discover what it is that gives you hope, pay more attention to it.

6. *Set a goal; get a purpose.* Remember, achieving goals builds hope. So set an attainable goal—and achieve it. Your goal can be running a mile, building a bookcase, or writing a song. Whatever it is, just make sure that your goal keeps your attention and challenges you. Set a date for reaching your goal, and figure out how to get there. Turn to others for assistance if you need it.

If you don't have a purpose in life, get one. Having a purpose connects you to other people. It's why you are here. Of course, you can have different purposes at different times in your life. In fact, the best part of finding yourself temporarily without a purpose is that you get to create a new one.

A person's purpose is usually related to his or her talents or abilities. Someone who is very outgoing and gregarious can help shy people become more sociable—perhaps by organizing social events at a nursing home. Someone who has a knack for fixing things can help the less handy keep their homes in good repair. Everyone has something to give. Figure out how to share your gifts, and you've found your purpose.

7. *Be your own "thought police."* Make sure your mind obeys the laws of hope. If you catch yourself constantly thinking hopeless thoughts, switch gears. Instead of dwelling on the difficulties in life, think about the good things—your child, a pet, the flowers on the windowsill. And if your difficulties are so overwhelming that you can't think of anything positive to focus on, make something up.

8. *Speak hope.* Like thoughts, words are powerful. Our minds hear them and pass them on to our bodies. For ages, wise men and women have claimed that humans have the power to speak things into existence. Now science has proved them right. So be careful what you say. If you want to be healthy, think healthy. Think and speak hope, not fear.

9. *Hope in the past.* Make your memories real. Most of us can remember times in our lives when some situations looked hopeless. And yet we survived. The memories of those times can be a powerful antidote to hopelessness when times get tough again. They remind us that things are almost never as hopeless as they seem.

To make the most of your hope-inspiring memories, make them accessible. If you are fortunate to have photographs that document some of the good times, keep them where you can see them and look at them often.

10. *Place hope in the future.* When you're struggling with serious illness or other difficulties, it's easy to become overwhelmed and forget the other, ongoing aspects of your life. But it's important to do so. Planning for the future is a way to defy hopelessness and create a light at the end of your tunnel. It's always a good idea to have plans for the future. Plan something for yourself that brings you happiness, no matter how temporary it is.

11. *Don't forget to laugh.* When all else fails, laughter succeeds. If you can still laugh, you are not defeated. Keep a journal of real-life events that make you laugh. You'll be surprised how funny they are the second—and third—time around.

CHAPTER 3
Understanding
Illness and Healing

Your willingness to take responsibility for your health care and aggressively seek out treatments can have a direct effect on your health. Research shows that when you are well-informed about your health, you can take better care of yourself. You'll feel more in control, and you'll experience less stress about your physical condition.

The best kind of medical care involves a partnership between you and your doctor. Your doctor needs information only you can provide. At the same time, you must follow your doctor's instructions precisely and listen carefully to all the information your doctor gives you.

Research shows that you will recover more quickly from illness if you understand what caused your condition, how a specific treatment can help, and how certain behavior or lifestyle changes can improve your chances of recovery.

MAKING DECISIONS

You must take control of your own health care decisions; you're the one who must call the shots. The ultimate decisions are up to you—despite the advice your doctors give you. Studies have shown that the more involved you are in your health care—the more in control you feel and the more you know—the better and more quickly you'll recover. Consider the following scenario:

Sue and Karen had cesarean section deliveries at about the same time. Sue had her surgery in a large, modern city hospital that specialized in women's health care, while Karen went to a small rural hospital.

Nurses explained to Sue that she would feel pain from the surgery. While in recovery at the hospital, Sue was given a morphine IV drip that could be self-administered by simply pushing a button. The IV drip allowed Sue to be completely in control of her own pain medication.

Karen, on the other hand, was not given the morphine IV drip. In fact, most of the time, she was left alone in her private room. The nurses told her that if she felt pain, she could ring the nurses' station for acetaminophen.

In no time, Sue was up and about, caring for her new baby. "I had no pain because of the morphine," she explains. "I felt empowered since I was able to administer my own pain medication. I felt like I was in control." Sue was able to manage her pain effectively: Because she could determine when she needed more pain medication, she was able to administer the morphine *before* the pain became too severe.

Karen, on the other hand, lying in bed and suffering from post-cesarean pain, hesitated to call the nurses' station to ask for medication. "The nurses made me feel that if I asked for pain medicine, I was weak," she said. And, because the nurses seemed so busy, Karen was too intimidated to "bother" them by asking for medication. "Also, I was worried that taking drugs might affect the baby, since I was nursing," she said. (Sue had been told by the nursing staff in her hospital that, even though she was nursing, her baby wouldn't be harmed by the morphine.)

Karen spent her recovery in the hospital feeling depressed, weepy, and in pain. "I felt disoriented and totally inept," she recalls. "No one bothered to tell me what was happening, what to expect. Nurses would come in and take the baby, bring the baby back, without speaking to me about what was going on. It seemed to take forever to recover from the surgery."

Sue sailed through her recovery. She felt confident that she could care for her new baby, and she was released from the hospital a day before Karen, even though they had their surgeries at the same time. "I couldn't imagine recovering from such major abdominal surgery without the morphine," Sue says now. "But I felt completely in control and very sure of myself." Karen, on the other hand, felt despondent, dependent, and utterly unable to cope. "It wasn't until I got home—and away from those nurses—that I really felt like myself again, capable of caring for my baby."

The difference between the experiences of the two women above is an example of the power of patient education—

how feeling in control cannot only empower you but can actually make you heal faster and better.

Being educated and feeling in control have psychological and physical benefits. When you don't understand your health problems, you tend to feel out of control and helpless, just the way Karen felt. Helplessness (and hopelessness) leads to extraordinary stress, which, as you've seen in earlier chapters, impairs your immune system. An impaired immune system hampers your body's ability to recover from illness and fight off disease.

Research shows that how you cope with illness or actual treatment procedures may affect how well you recover. If you refuse to be a passive hospital patient and demand full participation in your health care, for example, you'll recover more quickly than patients who placidly accept whatever it is their doctors tell them.

In addition, being involved in your own health care can influence your health by combating a sense of hopelessness. For example, in one recent study at the Western Consortium for Public Health in Berkeley, Calif., researchers found that men who said they had an overriding sense of hopelessness were less likely to survive heart disease and cancer. (This sense of hopelessness was also strongly linked to new cases of heart disease and cancer.)

The study involved 2,428 men aged 42 to 60, living in Finland, who participated in an ongoing study of psychological contributions to cardiovascular disease. Over 10 years, a Finnish registry recorded 174 deaths in the study sample. Half the deaths were caused by cardiovascular disease; most of the rest resulted from cancer, violence, or injury. The registry also noted 73 new cancer cases and 95 first-time heart attacks.

Men reporting moderate to high hopelessness died from all recorded causes at two to three times the rate of those reporting low or no hopelessness; the former group also developed cancer and heart attacks more frequently.

Physiologic effects of prolonged hopelessness that contribute to physical disease remain poorly understood. Men who feel hopeless may experience surges of stress hormones, which can undermine the heart or other internal organs, or they may undergo immune changes leading to cancer. It's also possible that, over the course of the study, the men who felt hopeless increased their poor health habits (smoking or drinking more), thereby endangering their health even further.

On the other hand, feeling hopeful and in control during stressful health situations has been shown to enhance your coping skills. In one study of older nursing home patients, researchers investigated the effects of giving residents more choices and more control over day-to-day events. Residents

Hope, Faith & Healing

who were encouraged to maintain control over their own lives became more active and reported feeling less unhappy than the residents who were encouraged to give up control and allow the nursing home staff to care for them.

Patients who were given the responsibility of making their own decisions were significantly more alert and involved in a range of activities—especially social activities. In the six months following the study, the group who had been given more control over their situations showed continued improvement in health. The difference between the two groups was apparent even in their death rates: 18 months after the study, only 15 percent of those who felt in control had died, compared with 30 percent of the group who did not feel in control.

The study also found that feelings of responsibility are particularly relevant for patients who must cope with long-term treatment plans that aren't easily monitored by their doctors (such as patients who must take medicine for high blood pressure, heart disease, or diabetes).

Fifty years ago, doctors didn't understand the value of helping patients understand their illness and treatment. If anything, experts went out of their way to keep patients in the dark, believing that knowing too much about their condition might actually interfere with their health care. Terminally ill patients often were not told about the true nature of their disease, since doctors believed they were "better off" not knowing the reality—or even the severity—of their condition.

Today, just the opposite is true, however. Information helps prepare you for upcoming treatments. Information helps you change your behavior and make good health care decisions. Information about your illness, treatment, or prevention can prepare you for what lies ahead. Research suggests that advance warnings combined with reassurance can help "inoculate" you against upcoming stressful experiences.

For example, if you are aware that your chemotherapy is likely to make you sick, you will be better able to handle the side effects than someone who didn't know about them. This sort of advance warning helps you anticipate discomfort or pain, start working through anxiety or grief, and make plans for effective coping, such as building a solid support system of friends and family. Advanced warnings give you a sense of control over threatening events.

THE TREATMENT TEAM

Today, if you are diagnosed with a serious illness, your doctor most likely will include you in a "treatment team," a group of specialists who work together to treat your health condition. Research has shown that this team approach is the best way to help patients handle an illness or injury.

In addition to doctors and nurses, there may be all sorts of health care professionals on your health care team. Physicians' assistants and nurse practitioners, for example, examine patients, diagnose some health conditions, and suggest courses

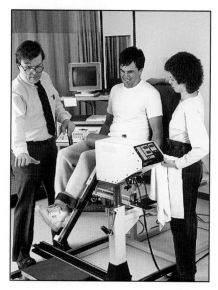

of treatment under a doctor's supervision. If you're injured or disabled, occupational therapists help you to regain the ability to carry out everyday tasks; physical therapists help you to regain lost physical function, using exercise, massage, or even ultrasound. Psychologists diagnose and treat mental health problems through techniques such as counseling and therapy. Psychiatrists are medical doctors who can prescribe medication and who also diagnose and treat mental illness. Radiology technicians take and develop X rays, CT scans, MRIs, and other types of radiation tests. Recreational therapists use group activities—including music and games—to help improve the communication or behavior patterns of withdrawn or depressed patients. Registered dieticians help specify the types of food that you should eat to improve your condition. Respiratory therapists use respirators and other devices to improve your breathing ability and capacity. Social workers counsel you about health-related and social problems, and can help you find financial aid, care after leaving the hospital, and other necessary services. Speech therapists treat disorders and

Your Health History

When meeting with a new doctor or treatment team, the process of education goes both ways. You'll want to show your doctor that you are an intelligent, concerned, and savvy health care consumer willing to participate in your own care. One good way to do this is to bring along your own health history. It should contain:

• name, address, marital status, and next of kin
• family history (age and health status of parents, grandparents, siblings, spouse, children). Your doctor will be especially interested in your family history of heart disease, cancer, high blood pressure, diabetes, arthritis, allergies, asthma, alcoholism, mental illness, or obesity.
• childhood illnesses (rubeola, rubella, polio, whooping cough, mumps, chicken pox, scarlet fever, rheumatic fever, and strep throat)
• adult illnesses
• psychiatric illness (including depression or anxiety)
• injuries (fractures, burns, or head injuries)
• hospitalizations
• operations
• current medications (prescription, over the counter, and home remedies)
• use of alcohol and other drugs, including tobacco

injuries that affect your ability to speak. Doctors of osteopathy are trained and licensed in the treatment of the musculoskeletal system.

Hope, Faith & Healing

Your health care team will explain your options and the pros and cons of each possible treatment. You'll be welcome to solicit second opinions—some insurance companies even require it—before any particular treatment is chosen. You even may be referred to a host of support groups that exist for the express purpose of educating patients who suffer from a particular disease or injury.

Every decision the health care team makes should involve the patient. In fact, today's doctors usually welcome the input of an educated patient. Studies have shown that those who lie in a hospital bed waiting to die often become helpless and hopeless—they give up, they lose the will to live, and so they die. An active, involved patient who approaches treatment with a positive, can-do attitude has a better chance of surviving.

Most health care workers believe that patients with chronic illnesses are entitled to the information they need to participate actively in—and assume responsibility for—much of their own health care. Health education can help a patient adapt to illness, cooperate with treatment, and learn problem-solving techniques. An educated patient can avoid being rehospitalized, which often happens when a patient doesn't understand how to care for a chronic condition. Patient education also saves patients money, since it can cut down on the length of hospital stays. Whether or not you want to learn what your health care workers can teach you, it's in your best interests to learn everything you can about your condition.

Hope, Faith & Healing

While many people want to assume responsibility for their own health care, they usually don't know how. Most people don't have the basic training to understand health and illness—and you can't respond to a health crisis without understanding the facts. There's plenty of information in your local library about how the body functions as well as information on specific diseases, treatments, and prognoses. As a patient, it's your job to read and digest this information so you can really understand how to help yourself—and manage your condition.

Research has shown that the more knowledge you have, the more willing you'll be to assume responsibility for your personal health. Once you become informed and stimulated, you'll become more motivated to eat better, exercise, stop smoking, and learn to reduce stress. When you accept responsibility for your own health, you can:

- learn what your needs are and how to meet them
- act assertively
- understand that symptoms are feedback from your body
- stop feeling like a helpless victim
- work on what you want to happen
- cultivate a basic sense of well-being
- trust that you have what you need within you

According to the Wellness Resource Center in Mill Valley, Calif., wellness is enhanced when a person assumes more responsibility for physical, mental, and emotional health. You can do this in a number of ways. First, you can be aware of your own body by using biofeedback, massage, or other types of body-awareness techniques that help you release stress.

Second, you can take care of your body and think of your own health needs by following a good diet, getting plenty of exercise, and cutting out poor health habits such as smoking or abusing alcohol. Finally, you can learn to take control of your mind. Counseling can help you create life circumstances as you want them and help you eliminate stress-producing habits, thoughts, and attitudes.

INFORMED CONSENT

To make sure you are informed of all risks involved in your treatment, doctors must abide by a rule called "informed consent." The Patient Self-Determination Act, which became effective in December 1991, requires that health care facilities (including hospitals and nursing homes) assure that patients are informed of their right to consent to or refuse treatment. The Patient Self-Determination Act requires your doctor to ex-

Hope, Faith & Healing

plain the risks that are involved in a particular treatment. (Sometimes you may be asked to sign a form stating that this information has been explained to you. It may be helpful to have a family member included in the discussion.)

Remember that you have the ultimate control of your body—and you have the the right to refuse any treatment. Depending on your particular situation, your doctor may be required to explain:

• the diagnosis
• the nature of the treatment
• any risks or side effects
• consequences of not receiving this particular treatment
• alternative treatments available

TREATMENT REGIMEN

The best medicines and the most up-to-date medical technology won't do anything if you can't—or won't—follow your doctor's instructions. One of the biggest issues in health care is "patient nonadherence," or "patient noncompliance"—patients who don't follow their doctors' orders about treatment. Studies have found that up to half of all patients don't follow their doctors' orders, and up to three-quarters of all medicines are taken incorrectly.

You can't hope to get better if you don't follow the directions. Many patients don't follow their doctors' orders when it comes to taking medication. After a few days on antibiotic

Following Treatment

A wide range of studies have investigated who is most and least likely to follow a doctor's treatment plan. Factors influencing how well you might follow the plan include:

- your age, sex, race, income level, and education
- severity of your illness
- how well your symptoms respond to treatment
- how complex your treatment plan is
- side effects
- your intelligence
- your attitude toward your health care team
- whether you accept your illness or not
- your religious beliefs
- expense of your treatment plan

therapy, for example, most patients begin to feel better, so they throw the rest of the pills away. But just because your symptoms disappear doesn't mean the infection has been eliminated; most likely, it's still lurking in your body. The infection may even recur as soon as you stop taking the antibiotics—or the infection can remain in your body and become immune to the antibiotic you originally used.

Adhering to a treatment regimen means you may have to make some changes in your lifestyle. In addition to taking medication, you may need to go on a special diet, cut back on some of your activities, watch out for symptoms, make follow-up appointments, and so on. Unfortunately, research has shown that the longer or more complex the treatment plan is, the less likely patients are to follow the directions.

You're most likely to follow directions if you really understand your illness and how your treatment plan will help you. This becomes especially important for older patients, who may be dealing with several different diseases or conditions at the same time. Managing a variety of medications and conditions can get very confusing. In addition, older patients may be 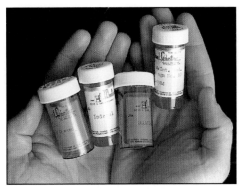 more sensitive to certain medications and suffer unexpected reactions. And, if older patients do not have a good support system, they may have trouble getting to and from their doctors' offices for their appointments. For these reasons, we all need to take the time to offer our help and support to the elderly who are dealing with a health condition or chronic illness.

WHAT TO EXPECT FROM YOUR DOCTOR

You should feel that you and your doctor are partners working together toward a common goal: making you well again.

You shouldn't feel afraid about asking your doctor a question. Instead, envision your doctor as an expert consultant who is available to help you with your health care choices. Your doctor should not dictate your treatment but, instead, present treatment options with explanations.

When Sharon was taken to a local hospital emergency room with an infection related to her cancer treatment, she resisted being admitted to the hospital. She'd been battling cancer for some time and had only just been released from the hospital a day or so earlier. Unwilling to face the seriousness of her present condition, she asked the doctor to let her go home.

"He looked me right in the eye very calmly and said 'If you go home now, you will be dead in three days.' He then went on to explain that the infection could be treated and since I'd been responding so well to the cancer treatment, there was every chance I could recover if I stayed in the hospital where the infection could be treated."

Her doctor recognized that Sharon's wish to leave the hospital was based on her emotions. By calmly explaining the options—but leaving the decision up to her—he helped Sharon make a rational, informed decision. "He didn't tell me what to do, but explained the situation in a way that I understood very clearly. And now I'm here to talk about it."

Most of the time, however, patients want more information than their doctors provide. And, unfortunately, researchers have found that a doctor's willingness to provide this information differs according to racial lines: Studies have shown that white patients tend to receive more information from their doctors than African-American and Hispanic patients.

It's also true that doctors tend to talk more to patients who ask questions. Thus, it's a good idea to arrive at your office visits with a list of your concerns. Remember, it's your doctor's job to answer your questions—don't worry that you're taking up too much of his or her time. And don't hesitate to write down the information that your doctor gives you. It's often hard to remember important information when you're feeling nervous, scared, or ill. Things that seem crystal clear in the doctor's office may be jumbled up in your mind by the time you arrive home.

Indeed, studies have shown that most patients remember only about half of everything they are told by their physicians. Recommendations about lifestyle changes are forgotten even quicker than are doctors' directions about medicines. This is why you should take the time to write down any information your doctor gives you.

It's important to discuss your concerns with your doctor. Sometimes, you may not even realize you've been misinformed about a procedure or a condition until you start talking with your doctor. (You may be surprised to find out that your friends or family, though their intentions were good, may have given you incorrect information.) Your doctor may offer a combination of strategies to help educate you about your

Hope, Faith & Healing

disease, including counseling, group classes, audiovisual aids, or written material. You may even be referred to community resources, such as the American Cancer Society, Alcoholics Anonymous, or the National Institute of Mental Health.

Ideally, your doctor will talk to you not just about what you need to know, but also about what you need to do. Some doctors may help you write an action plan based on the goals you need to accomplish in order to heal. Your doctor may also schedule a follow-up appointment or telephone call within the next few weeks to evaluate your progress.

Teaching Techniques

There are many methods that your health care professional may use to help educate you about your condition. Most often, however, doctors will simply explain what your condition is, how you got it (if possible), and how it can be treated. It's important during this time, however, that you express your concerns and feelings, ask questions, write down your doctor's responses, and ask for clarification about any misunderstandings you have.

Demonstration and practice are key ingredients to any learning situation, especially if there are specific skills that need to be mastered. If special equipment is needed to help you manage your condition (such as a colostomy bag, syringe, or dressing), your health care worker should show you how to use the equipment properly and with confidence.

Community Programs

There are a wide variety of health educational programs offered free (or for a small fee). You may find programs at your local health care agencies about:

- smoking cessation
- prenatal care
- babysitting
- grandparenting
- weight reduction
- caring for aging parents
- exercise
- coping with chronic illness (support groups)

Teaching aids—pamphlets, books, pictures, films, slides, audio or video tapes, programmed instruction, or computerized learning modules—can be an invaluable way to learn more about your condition or health problem. But even with the best aids, a single learning session may not be enough, so don't be afraid to ask for more help. Follow-up sessions can help boost your confidence level about your ability to follow through with what you've learned.

Some patients prefer to learn about their disease in a group environment. In a group situation, patients can learn about their condition from each other, and at the same time, gain moral support and encouragement. And, as you'll learn in the

Hope, Faith & Healing

next chapter, "Social Support and Healing," having a support network can be crucial to maintaining your health. But, even if you're involved in a group environment, you'll still need to touch base with your health care professional to make sure all of your questions are being answered.

YOUR RESPONSIBILITY AS A PATIENT

Being responsible for your own health care isn't easy. In fact, sometimes it can be downright intimidating. Usually, the time when it's most important to work with your doctor is when you or a loved one is sick or hurt. It's during these times that feelings of helplessness and fear can make it especially hard to communicate. As a patient, you should expect the following from your health care professional:

- to be given as much medical information as you want about your illness
- to have a reasonable amount of time to ask your questions
- to receive information about how much your health care or a procedure or test will cost
- to know where to go in an emergency
- to have reasonable access to your doctor (But be realistic: Don't expect last-minute appointments.)
- to be seen within a reasonable amount of time during a scheduled appointment
- to be able to change physicians or get a second opinion at any time

- to expect that your medical information will be quickly forwarded to a new doctor or hospital
- to be assured that your condition and records will remain private (For certain conditions, however, your doctor is required by law to notify government officials.)
- to participate in decisions about your health care based on information about your illness

Of course, you have certain responsibilities toward your doctor as well. You should be on time for your appointments. If you have to cancel an appointment, call at least 24 hours in advance. Write down the questions you plan to ask *before* you arrive. If you don't understand something, stop the discussion with your doctor and ask for more information; don't call him at the office three days later for clarification.

Once your doctor prescribes a treatment, follow it exactly. If you can't, tell your doctor. If you're interested in trying a different treatment, let your doctor know. Be patient—most treatments don't work overnight. Inform your doctor immediately if you experience any side effects, worsened symptoms, or complications.

A SECOND OPINION

It's almost standard practice to get a second opinion these days—and many insurance companies require it before approving some types of surgery. Either you or your doctor can decide to seek another opinion. A good doctor should not have any qualms about referring you to a specialist to have the diagnosis confirmed.

A second opinion also may be a good idea if the diagnosis is clear but the treatment possibilities are uncertain. Many diseases have several treatment options. A second opinion may be in your best interest if a diagnosis is serious, if the treatment is risky, experimental, or controversial, or if major surgery seems necessary.

Don't hesitate to pursue a second opinion. Let your doctor know you'd like a second opinion to confirm the diagnosis or to discuss alternative treatments.

WHEN TO CHANGE DOCTORS

A good doctor will welcome your active role in your health care. You should be able to bring up concerns or questions without feeling intimidated. But, unfortunately, not all doctors welcome active patient participation.

Sarah, a medical writer in a large metropolitan city, cared for her grandmother who had leukemia. Because her grandmother didn't understand her condition very well, she asked Sarah to help her make sense of what the doctors were telling her. Sarah's writing often focused on cancer, so she was somewhat familiar with many of the newer treatments that were being developed at some of the nation's leading health care institutions. When she called her grandmother's hematologist to discuss her grandmother's care and condition, Sarah framed her questions very carefully.

"I didn't know this doctor, but I have known physicians who are very defensive about their treatment recommendations. When I spoke to this doctor, I very calmly and politely asked him for his opinion on one of the new treatments I knew had been effective with my grandmother's type of leukemia.

"I phrased my question with extreme delicacy, asking him whether he felt this new treatment had any worth. He became extremely defensive at once, and said to me with a sneer, 'What medical school did you graduate from?'"

Sarah was furious. She had not been dictating to the doctor that this newer treatment be used. She felt that a more helpful physician would have simply explained the value—or risk—of the procedure.

So, take your time in selecting your doctor—it's important for your physical well-being and peace of mind. If you answer "yes" to any of the following statements, consider looking for another doctor. In general, do you feel that your doctor:

• isn't trustworthy?
• resents your questions?
• makes you uncomfortable when talking about personal aspects of your illness?
• is condescending or abrupt?
• is not always straightforward or honest?
• isn't giving you his or her complete attention?

- rushes you through your appointment?
- is often not available?
- has inadequate after-hours coverage?
- has a lifestyle or philosophy that is incompatible with yours?
- fails to follow through on problems when they crop up?

How do you go about finding a new doctor? First, assemble a list of names. Ask friends or relatives for recommendations. Check with your county medical society, which should be able to give you a list of physicians in your area. Consumer affairs groups may also have this information. Try checking with your local health care center or hospital (some hospitals have free doctor referral services that can match you up with a list of doctors). Look in the yellow pages of your local phone book. You can also find several medical directories in your local library that list physicians and their credentials.

When you start to narrow down your list, take into account the information you've received from friends and family—about availability, promptness in returning phone calls, bedside manner, and so on. Also, you should only consider doctors who are located near your home or place of business; you aren't likely to keep those appointments that are too far out of your way.

When you arrive at the doctor's office, you will probably speak to a receptionist or a medical assistant. Introduce yourself and explain that you're looking for a physician. Do you like the receptionist's tone of voice? Is he or she warm and friendly or brusque and impatient? Are your questions answered directly?

Ask what hospital the doctor is affiliated with, his or her office hours and availability on weekends or evenings, the fee schedules for checkups and office visits, and whether they accept your insurance plan. Ask about office coverage when the

doctor isn't available and how much time the doctor allots for each appointment. (An initial exam should last at least a half hour; subsequent office visits should last at least 10 minutes.) If you have particularly strong religious beliefs that may affect your health care, you should ask about the doctor's willingness to accommodate your concerns.

With this information, you should be able to narrow down your list to two or three doctors. Now call back the receptionists and ask for an appointment for a brief consultation. When you arrive for your appointment, take note of the condition of the office. Is it clean, comfortable, and cheerful? Are you greeted pleasantly by the doctor's staff? How long do you have to wait before seeing the doctor?

When you meet the doctor, ask yourself whether:

• the doctor seems to care about you as a person

Online Health Information

The following Internet patient-education resources and World Wide Web sites may provide the information you need to take control of your health care.

- Centers for Disease Control and Prevention (http://www.cdc.gov/)
- Diseases, Disorders and Related Topics (http://www.mic.ki.se/Diseases/index.html)
- HealthLinks (http://www.hslib.washington.edu)
- Healthtouch Online (http://www.healthtouch.com/level1/menu.htm)
- Healthwise (http://www.columbia.edu/cu/healthwise/)
- MedAccess (http://www.medaccess.com/)
- MedWeb (http://www.emory.edu/WHSCL/medweb.html)
- Medscape (http://www.medscape.com)
- National Health Information Center (http://nhic-nt.health.org)
- National Institutes of Health (http://www.nih.gov)
- National Institute of Mental Health (http://www.nimh.nih.gov)
- National Clearinghouse for Alcohol and Drug Information (http://www.health.org)
- American Academy of Pediatrics (http://www.aap.org)
- The U.S. National Library of Medicine (http://www.nlm.nih.gov)
- OncoLink (http://www.oncolink.upenn.edu)
- Harvard Medical Web (http://www.med.harvard.edu)

- you feel comfortable talking to the doctor
- you feel relaxed or rushed
- the doctor uses a lot of medical jargon
- you are encouraged to ask questions

Is your meeting with the doctor a positive or negative experience? If it's a positive one, you may have found the doctor you've been looking for. If not, move on to the next doctor on your list.

PREVENTION

Becoming educated about your health is important—not just in treating disease but in preventing illness as well. It is up to you to stay healthy. Your doctor can tell you that smoking is dangerous, but only you can make the decision to throw the cigarettes away. Only you can make the decision to follow a healthy diet, to take your medicine, to exercise, and to learn how to control your stress by using relaxation techniques.

One of the biggest problems with digesting your doctor's advice on taking preventive measures is that, deep down, we don't really believe that we will get sick. Cancer, heart disease, mental illness, and other serious diseases are problems that happen to other people—not to us or those we love. Of course, believing that we are immune to serious illness, aging, or death will, ultimately, only get in the way of both prevention and recovery.

Many patients want access to all the information that health providers have about a disease or condition, including ongoing clinical trials or names of top researchers in the field. In

addition to information that your doctor can give you, there are many consumer health information books available in bookstores and libraries. Some

hospitals also have patient education libraries, which may be professionally staffed and maintained. There are also a growing number of health-oriented audio and video tapes you can buy or rent (or even obtain free from your local library) that can provide more information.

Other useful information can be found on the online services and the Internet (see box, page 122). If you don't have online access at home or at your place of business, visit your local public library. Many library branches now offer complete online access. To locate informative health sites, ask the librarian for assistance.

In addition, there are many health-related organizations and support groups that can provide free information on specific diseases. To find their addresses and phone numbers, look in the yellow pages of your phone book, or in the *Encyclopedia of Associations* available in most public libraries.

Never give up the responsibility for your health out of a feeling of helplessness—or hopelessness. No situation ever needs to be beyond your control. You will always have the option—indeed, the obligation—to ask questions, change your mind, and discuss your fears. If you're sick, you may not be able to change the diagnosis, but you can—and should—be involved in the decisions about your care and treatment.

CHAPTER 4
Social Support and Healing

You're sitting around your kitchen table, sharing a joke and pizza with old friends. You're feeling good, you're laughing, you're having a good time. You're also getting healthy.

Whether you call it intimacy, friendship, or just plain companionship, having good relationships with people is more than just fun—it can keep illness and death at bay.

The mind and body are inextricably entwined. We now know that how you *feel* can affect how healthy you are. Scores of recent studies prove that this mind-body link affects your general health: It seems that folks who have close, loving relationships—whether it's with friends, family, or even pets—tend to live the longest and healthiest lives.

EMOTIONS AND YOUR BODY

At first, it may seem hard to believe that having a friend could influence whether or not you get the flu! But when you understand a bit more about how the body works—how it fights disease and how it creates and expresses emotions—you'll see that your relationships can have a very real impact on your health.

For several decades, in a variety of intriguing studies, researchers tracked hundreds of thousands of people, investigating who got sick and who didn't and what these people had in common. They studied what the participants ate and drank, what they did for a living, and whether they believed in God. They looked at their friendships and family members, at their bad habits and good, how much they exercised, what hobbies they had, how much sleep they got, and what their medical histories revealed. And what the scientists found surprised many skeptics. Among other things, their studies revealed:

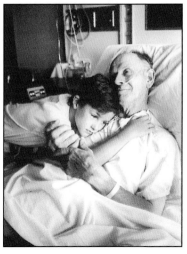

- Touching patients helps them recover more quickly
- Being in love helps to protect against colds
- Having relationships helps you live longer
- Knowing you're loved helps you recover more quickly
- Having a pet helps you survive disease

When scientists studied four types of social connections—marriage, contact with family and friends, church membership, and group affiliations—they discovered how different types of social bonds could affect longevity. The researchers found that those who had the weakest social connections were twice as likely to die in the next nine years as those with the strongest ties. In fact, the relationship between social isolation and death is as strong as the relationship between smoking and death or high blood cholesterol levels and death.

THE LANGUAGE OF LOVE

Do you feel giddy when you first fall in love? Does your heart start to beat a little faster when you think of something romantic? Does your stomach knot when a relationship that's important to you hits a rocky patch? Anyone who has ever felt a physical jolt in response to a strong emotion has experienced this link between mind and body. That's because, believe it or not, your body experiences "love"—like all emotions—in a very basic molecular way.

It may not seem very romantic, but, according to Candace Pert, Ph.D., pharmacologist and professor at Georgetown University in Washington, D.C., the essence of emotion can be traced to a class of brain chemicals known as *endorphins*. The job of these endorphins (a type of chemical called a *neurotransmitter*) is to carry messages between your brain cells. These little chemical messengers are constantly "talking" to more than 100 trillion cells throughout your body, including those in your muscles, your stomach, and your heart. It is these same endorphins that can ease pain when you are hurt. Endorphins are also responsible for the natural "high" that runners—even walkers and bicyclists—experience after completing a couple of fast laps around the neighborhood.

But these endorphins do much more than make you feel good or ease your pain. Endorphins also communicate with the cells that make up your immune system—your body's own army of germ-fighters. Endorphins strengthen the immune system. When your endorphin levels are high, your immune system becomes stronger. As your endorphin levels rise, you get sick less often. And, if you do get sick, not to worry: A strong immune system will help speed your recovery.

The emotional connections you make with other people also influence your endorphin levels. Studies suggest that even the slightest gestures of emotional support—a touch, a hug, a smile—can trigger a burst of endorphins. Thus, each time you hug your child or kiss your spouse, you trigger these feel-good chemicals. And, as you now know, this release of endorphins ultimately helps to strengthen your immune system.

Is it any wonder that people who are "in love" have fewer colds and more active immune systems? Then it shouldn't come as a surprise to you that married folks tend to be a lot healthier than people who are unattached.

Our brains secrete hormones and neurotransmitters during times of stress. This survival mechanism probably originated in prehistoric times to ensure the continuation of the species. Imagine a caveman in the wilderness on the trail of a wooly mammoth. Suddenly, right behind him, he hears the roar of a saber-toothed tiger. To survive, he either has to fight or run away, and his body needs to make that decision immediately.

The central nervous system responds to this "fight or flight" directive by pumping "stress chemicals" through your body. The three important stress chemicals are the hormones norepinephrine, epinephrine, and cortisol.

Norepinephrine's role in the body is to boost heart rate and blood pressure. Epinephrine's job is to release sugar into the blood. Cortisol plays a major role in protein breakdown and formation, blood sugar control, and reduction of inflammation. Cortisol is also necessary to mount an effective response against severe stress due to disease or injury.

Modern-day Americans have the same fight or flight mechanism as our prehistoric ancestors, even though most of us don't face the same death-defying situations in our day-to-day lives. Instead, our stress response is triggered by a host of daily stresses or by our emotions—by the difficult feelings of loneliness and loss, by feeling disconnected with those around us, by feeling as though we don't belong. Stress can be set off by an

How the Brain Works

The link between mind and body is real and far more complex than we ever before realized. Your brain is more than an isolated organ, and your body is more than a network of nerves and organs designed to carry out commands from the brain. Instead, the mind and the body work together, more so than anything we could have imagined even 20 years ago.

The brain and the body interact in four different ways:

• Through nerves that control the muscles
• Through nerves that control involuntary actions like heart rate and artery size
• Via hormones that affect breasts, glands, ovaries or testes, and kidneys
• Via neurotransmitters that affect body systems, including the immune system

It is apparent, then, that the brain and the body interact in a thousand different ways. This physical interrelation can help explain how something like social support—which affects the brain—can be translated into physical responses in the body.

argument with your spouse, by a missed bill payment, or by an overdue library book. Whatever the stressful situation, the result is the same: The body is flooded with stress chemicals.

These momentary bouts of stress don't seem to have a strong impact on the body. In most people, once the source of

Hope, Faith & Healing

the stress is removed, the body's chemical levels go back to normal, and all is well. You get over the argument, you pay the overdue bill, you return your library book. Your stress is relieved, you feel more relaxed, and your immune system suffers no permanent harm.

But some people seem to live in a constant state of stress. For these folks, it feels as though their stress response never stops. They live in a constant state of arousal; their bodies are constantly ready to fight or flee.

This type of relentless stress can depress the immune system, making your body more vulnerable to disease. People who are depressed or bereaved, for example, often experience a gradual slowdown in immune function. (Constant stress can also affect personality. Some individuals may feel tense and explosive or feel hopeless or helpless.)

Ultimately, the immune system loses much of its ability to fight disease. As the immune system continues to break down, the body begins to lose its battles with invading disease organisms. As a result, you become sick more often. If you can intercept the stress-induced flood of chemicals, you'll have a better chance of staying healthy. One way of doing this is by developing a base of social support—people with whom you can vent your frustration, anger, and other negative emotions.

Social support is the help we get from other people. This physical and/or emotional assistance can come from a spouse, a child, a friend, or a social or community contact such as a church or club. Social support can influence your behavior. For example, it can promote such healthy behaviors as adherence to medical regimens, adequate sleep, healthy diet, and moderate alcohol use. Recent studies suggest that success in stopping smoking has also been linked to support from spouses and friends.

Loneliness and Heart Disease

If you're isolated and alone, you're more likely to be depressed than if you are married or in a committed relationship, according to a recent Duke University Medical Center study. And if you are depressed and alone, you're also more likely to have poor physical health. Thus, treating depression is important. Studies show a patient's social situation and mindset can make or break even the best of modern medical care, according to Redford Williams, M.D., director of the behavioral medicine program at Duke and chief investigator for the Duke study.

Dr. Williams believes that enrolling a heart attack patient in a social support group—or even giving them a phone call to see how they're doing—can be just as important to a successful recovery as the actual medical procedures. That's because patients who survive a heart attack but are depressed are five times more likely to die within six months than those who aren't depressed. Most of the time that depression is linked to whether or not the patient has some kind of social support.

People with good social support often have strong immune systems, despite the different types of stress in their lives. For example, studies have shown that medical students who live with supportive friends or families tend to have healthier immune systems than do those students who live alone. It appears that, for some people, having a strong social support system can offset the unhealthy aspects of stress. And among those people with the strongest immune systems are those who are happily married.

HEALTH BENEFITS OF MARRIAGE

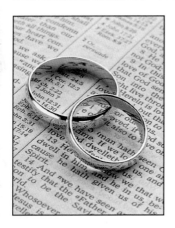 For more than a hundred years, researchers have known that married couples have lower death rates from a whole range of different diseases than single people do. And the health of married people can't be explained away by assuming that people who get married—and stay that way—are just healthier to begin with. Researchers at UCLA have found that, for a variety of reasons, it's the state of marriage *itself* that has the most impact on maintaining good health.

The Framingham Heart Study—which has tracked the health of 5,000 people for the past 30 years—found, among other things, that getting and staying married is a predictor of

Hope, Faith & Healing

Finding Social Support

The combined stress of career, husband, and kids can trigger health problems for working moms. A social support program can head off health woes by helping busy moms make friends.

According to a Duke University Medical Center study, moms who attended weekly support-group training sessions on stress management boosted their level of social support. Those who benefited the most from the study were the married moms. Married moms usually have less time for outside social contacts. Participating in a support program helped them build social ties with other women, thus reducing their stress. According to study director Redford Williams, M.D., director of behavioral research at Duke, improved social support can reduce the risk of high blood pressure and heart disease in this high-risk group.

a long, healthy life. Other studies reveal that people who lead isolated lives are two to three times more at risk of dying at a young age than are people who feel connected to others. A study of more than 25,000 cancer patients found that married people were more likely to survive longer than single individuals. Married people were also more likely to have cancer diagnosed at earlier, more curable stages and to start treatment sooner. Even when members of the married group were diagnosed with cancer at more advanced stages, those who were married seemed to have the best odds for survival.

How can a wedding band possibly ward off disease? As we've already discovered, reaching out to another human being has a measurable, positive physical effect within your own body, boosting the levels of the endorphins and enhancing your own immune system. But there are other reasons why having a committed relationship might be good for your health.

Let's say you needed to undergo cancer treatment. You'll be expected to make countless trips to the hospital for drug treatment or radiation therapy. For some people, the effort of just getting out of bed in the morning can be overwhelming when they're suddenly faced with the reality of cancer—and the side effects of some cancer treatments may leave you too exhausted to even try. And, even if you want to go to the hospital to receive your treatments, if you live alone, you may not feel up to driving yourself there.

Being sick can be very overwhelming—especially if there's no one there to hold your hand, to speak up for you, or to ask questions when something doesn't make sense. Married people have a safety net of support that helps them better deal with stress and recover from illness.

If you're married, you're more likely to have someone who can help you keep your appointments, too. You're also more likely to feel you have a reason for getting better—your spouse needs you. Being married tends to bring about that sense of obligation. As a result, married people are more likely to take their medicine, work out, and even go to the doctor on a regular basis for their checkups.

And, odds are, if you're married, you're also likely to be eating a whole lot better than people who live alone. Married couples are much more likely to eat balanced meals at regular

That Lovin' Feeling

If you haven't found that perfect someone, don't despair. You're not doomed to a life of ill health. The good news is that any loving relationship can have health benefits. If you don't have a spouse, a live-in "significant other" works, too. It's the affection and attention, plus the commitment that a couple shares, that make you feel so good.

An extended family can also be health-giving. Keep tabs on each other's lives, health, and family gossip. It's a good way to stay in touch and create a network of social support.

If you live across the country, away from your relatives, and there's no future spouse or friend in sight, you can always get a pet. Studies show that animals can lower your blood pressure, ease your stress, and give you a positive outlook.

Any kind of companionship—even a coworker or an exercise buddy—can help boost your health. There are no age cutoffs, no rules, no limits. Just reach out and touch someone, and you'll be surprised at how much better you feel.

Hope, Faith & Healing

hours than are single people. All too often, single folks grab a burger on the run or eat a pork chop standing over the kitchen sink. After all, who needs the hassle of three square meals a day when you have to eat them all alone?

In addition to eating right, married couples also tend to lead more measured, traditional lives. Statistics show, for example, that attached men are less likely to be risky drivers. As a result, a man's auto insurance rates drop when he gets married.

Being married usually means you're a lot better off financially, too. That's probably because married couples tend to make more money than single people and are more conservative when it comes to saving it. And married men tend to make more money than single men. (In fact, studies by the Federal Reserve Board and Princeton University found that single men earn up to 50 percent less than married men of the same age, race, and education. Single men aren't losing out because of discrimination, however; married men consistently earn more money because they typically work harder and better.)

Studies have shown that married couples experience less economic stress and have better medical care. They eat more and better food. Odds are, married couples live in better houses and carry better (more expensive) health insurance. And married couples can usually better afford to get away from stress by taking vacations at least once a year.

It's clear that being married is the healthy way to go. But, surprisingly, the rewards of marriage aren't the same for men and women. The dramatic initial boost to men's health after marriage occurs, scientists say, because their health habits improve. Unmarried men are extraordinarily vulnerable to a wide range of health and lifestyle problems. Men who aren't attached are more likely to commit, and be a victim of, crimes. Single men are involved in more accidents of every variety. They drink more and deal more drugs. And single men rank lower in well-being and happiness than married men: Research shows that unattached men kill themselves three times more often than married men.

In addition to good health, another health benefit that comes from a good marriage is a positive self-image that is associated with being "part of a couple." (And a positive self-image can ultimately lead to less stress and better health.) Married people who are very independent of each other, however, separate themselves from that couple identity. And, without the couple identity, these individuals are more likely to suffer health problems.

DIVORCE AND HEALTH

The statistics linking marriage and health do suggest that those who are happily married receive the most health benefits. But we all know that being married is no guarantee that you are going to be happy—this country's sky-high divorce rate is testament to that. So what happens when the ties that bind begin to strangle, and the marriage fails?

What scientists tell us is that when the marriage ends, so do the health benefits. As soon as the divorce decree is signed, death rates of divorced men and women revert to the higher levels of their single friends. Divorced men are twice as likely to die prematurely from high blood pressure as married men. They are also twice as likely to die from heart disease, four times as likely to die prematurely from throat cancer, and seven times as likely to die prematurely from pneumonia. Moreover, scientists have known for 60 years that divorced men are at a tremendous risk for suicide. In fact, being divorced and a non-smoker is only slightly less dangerous than being married and smoking more than a pack of cigarettes a day.

This doesn't mean that if you find yourself in a bad marriage—filled with anger, recrimination, or violence—you should stay married for the sake of your health. Divorced people aren't as healthy as their happily married friends, but neither are married people who are very unhappy.

While a good marriage can make you healthier, a bad marriage can make you sick. Trying to survive in an unhappy marriage is not good for anyone's health. Study after study has shown that the stress chemicals that pour into your bloodstream when you feel angry, depressed, trapped, or hopeless can be devastating to your health. Besides, after divorce, some people are better able to discover those other sources of support that can boost their immune systems—extended family, friends, even church.

Losing a spouse to death is one of the most stressful experiences that can happen to you, second only to the death of your child. Surviving a spouse's death is, in fact, so stressful that it puts your health at risk.

Surviving the death of a spouse is especially difficult for men. Researchers at the Johns Hopkins University School of Hygiene and Public Health found that men have higher death and illness rates after they are widowed than married men of the same age, even after adjustment for the effects of socioeconomic level and behavior factors such as cigarette smoking, age at first marriage, and frequency of church attendance. The study, published in the *American Journal of Epidemiology* in 1981, found no significant differences in mortality rates between widowed and married females after adjustment for the same factors, however.

Why are men less likely to survive widowhood? Researchers suggest that widowers may have more trouble than women recovering from the death of a spouse because most men do not have strong social support networks to rely on in times of need. Psychologists report that men just don't have the same types of intimate relationships women do—not even with their own children. Most widows, on the other hand, can usually call on a wide-ranging safety net, knit with plenty of close friendships and lifelong relationships.

Women of all ages tend to maintain more close and nurturing relationships than do men, according to Lillian Rubin, Ph.D., a psychologist at the Institute for the Study of Social Change at the University of California at Berkeley. Men, if they have neglected friends and support groups all their lives, may have no one to turn to when their only means of social support is gone.

And, while marriage is good for your health, it doesn't mean that after the death of your spouse you should run out and get remarried. A marriage license isn't necessarily going to add extra years to your life. Married people still get sick, and they still die.

FRIENDS AND HEALING

Whether or not you're married is just one of a constellation of risk factors that come into play to create disease. An illness is almost never limited to one single cause. Maybe you live in a city with polluted air, or you drink water that isn't pure. Maybe you smoke, drink too much, or eat too many fats or sweets. Maybe you don't get enough sleep. Perhaps your job has been getting to you, and the stress is building up.

Hope, Faith & Healing

Sometimes, the reason you get sick is hard to determine. And while marriage can help maintain your health, those who aren't married needn't despair. There are plenty of other ways to build a support system that can provide health-giving benefits. The quality of your relationships and the depth of your social support also have an impact on your health. Practically any caring relationship—whether it's with a friend, confidant, or coworker—can make you healthier.

Making time for the people you care about will not only make you feel good, but it can help you live longer, too. Remember, your immune system can't tell the difference be-

tween a kiss from your spouse and a hug from a friend. It's the emotions you experience when you reach out to others—and when they reach

out to you—that are so beneficial to your health. Constant, caring relationships take work, but, in the long run, they're worth it.

Perhaps women tend to live longer than men because women are better at making—and keeping—strong emotional ties outside of marriage. After all, it's usually women who write letters, make social plans, reply to invitations, and spend hours chatting on the phone.

Intimacy is the hallmark of women's friendships. Very few men have these types of intimate relationships—men tend to *do* things, they don't *share* things. In a study of more than 300 people, Rubin discovered that very few of the men she interviewed could name a best friend. Those who did usually named a woman.

Our society has socialized most women to become adept at creating intimate relationships. Men just don't receive the same training. The tragedy in this difference is that the ability to reach out has a very real, very dramatic effect on how long we live and how healthy we are.

Since the 1970s, study after study has shown that friendship and social support are crucial to your health—and that, without such attachments, you're just not going to be quite as healthy

Are Two Enough? Are Six Too Many?

Studies show that social bonds are important to survival. But people appear to need only so many close relationships, according to psychologists at Case Western Reserve and Wake Forest universities.

Having two close relationships may make a world of difference to a person's health and happiness, say psychologists Ray F. Baumeister, Ph.D., and Mark R. Leary, Ph.D. But having more is not necessarily better. There is little difference in the health benefits of having eight friends compared with six.

as you should be. In fact, in one study of nearly 7,000 residents of Alameda County, Calif., researchers could predict who would die within the next nine years simply by counting how many social ties the participants had. Based on this study and others like it, the California Department of Health launched a public service program pleading with residents to "make a friend."

Friends can be good medicine indeed. A variety of social relationships can protect you from a wide range of potentially fatal diseases, ranging from tuberculosis to lung cancer to heart disease. In fact, one study found that people with lots of good friends had significantly less blockage of their coronary arteries than did those individuals who reported having very little social support in their lives.

If you still doubt the power of your emotions, take a moment to consider this: In one study, when nurses held the hands of female surgical patients while their vital signs were taken, those patients left the hospital sooner and recovered faster at home than did women who had no similar physical contact with hospital workers.

Even animal studies reveal the value of personal companionship and simple physical touch. One study of rabbits who were fed high-fat diets found that those who were talked to and petted developed much less artery-clogging fat deposits than the rabbits who received only routine treatment. Other studies show that animals who share their cages with companions have longer, healthier lives than those who live alone.

Hope, Faith & Healing

There's hope even for those who can't pass up an after-dinner cigarette. Studies show that even cigarette smokers have a lower risk of certain diseases if they have strong social support systems. Why? Friends can act as a buffer to the stress that we encounter day in and day out. Friends are also a good antidote to loneliness.

The support you get from friends is often less judgmental than the advice you receive from family members. Because of this, we may be more likely to confide in friends than family and seek them out in times of stress.

When we make mistakes, choose unwisely, or fail to achieve, it's often far less difficult to pour out our hearts to our friends than it is to our family members. In fact, one study found that having close female friends was vital to a woman's sense of well-being in her later years—even more so than marriage, children, or grandchildren.

Because the health benefits of social support are so powerful and the urge to belong is so strong, some scientists suspect that the impulse to connect with others may be encoded in our genes. A person who is cut off from others is likely to suffer both physically and psychologically. In fact, many of the strongest emotions that people experience—both good and bad—are linked to feeling a sense of belonging and social support. We want to form new social bonds—by joining a new club, making a new friend, having a new child—and we are usually very reluctant to break these bonds. How many of us continue to send holiday cards once a year to individuals we never see or even call on the phone? How many people seem reluctant to break off a bad relationship?

Our need to belong is deeply rooted. Like eating and sleeping, perhaps the urge to reach out to others is so strong because our very lives depend upon it: Without these relationships, our health is very likely to fail.

PETS AND HEALING

Marriage and friends are good for our health. But, of course, not everyone is happily married. Maybe you're divorced or your spouse has died. Maybe you've never been married at all. Maybe you've lost touch with friends, or you've retired and moved, leaving friends behind. Whatever the reason, you may be among those individuals who are often very much alone. But this doesn't mean you're destined to a bleak existence fraught with poor health. It means you need to seek out a little companionship. The solution to your loneliness may be right around the corner—at the nearest animal shelter.

In recent years, we have become increasingly aware of the role of animals in combating the loneliness of spirit that affects so many people, especially the elderly. Animals are indispensable companions for many lonely people, essential therapeutic tools for people with a variety of psychological and emotional problems, and vital helpers to many who are physically handicapped.

Hope, Faith & Healing

According to Aaron Katcher, M.D., an associate professor of psychiatry at the University of Pennsylvania, the feelings you experience when caring for another living creature can actually boost your health. Katcher believes the companionship of animals may actually reduce the frequency of serious disease, as well as prolong life.

How do animals improve our health? According to Katcher, the feelings of intimacy we experience with our pets can increase our resistance to disease in the same way that human companionship seems to boost health. The mere presence of an animal—even without direct contact—can lower blood pressure rates. In one study, children brought into an experimental setting had lower blood pressure when a dog was present with the experimenter, compared with when the experimenter was there alone. Blood pressure was lower in the presence of the dog both when the children were sitting quietly and when they were engaged in the mildly stressful task of reading aloud.

When people speak to each other, their blood pressure levels almost always increase. When people speak to their pets, however, their blood pressure levels remain the same or, in some cases, decrease. When we talk to an animal, the pattern of speech we use tends to be slower, softer, and higher pitched. Our sentences are often shorter. Research has shown that this style of speech is associated with lower blood pressure.

When people speak to animals, they often touch them. Touching can be an effective method of reducing stress. Stud-

Pets and Children

Studies show that youngsters derive special and unique relationships with their pets that are not the same as any other type of social relationship. In one study, kids rated pets high on both "love" and "companionship," but they rated their siblings high only on companionship, not love. Grandparents were rated high on love, but not companionship.

Only a pet—the family dog or cat—merited high marks in both categories, underlining the unique social support a pet can bring to a family.

How Animals Make Us Healthy

How can animals improve your health? Although more studies are needed to confirm the positive impact animals have on our health, Aaron Katcher, M.D., an associate professor of psychiatry at the University of Pennsylvania, suggests a pet can offer us the following healthy functions:

• Companionship
• Something that keeps you active
• Something to care for
• Something to touch
• Something to look at
• Something that makes you feel safe
• A stimulus for exercise
• A stimulus for play and laughter
• Something that gives constancy to life

ies have shown that, in patients recovering from heart attacks, the simple act of touching the patient when taking his pulse can alter the heart rate and lower the likelihood of abnormal heart rhythms.

In fact, any phenomenon that attracts our attention outward, away from our private worries and concerns, can reduce blood pressure. Techniques such as meditation that focus our gaze have been shown to interrupt thought patterns and reduce stress. In this way, staring into a tank of tropical fish can significantly reduce blood pressure in both hypertensive and healthy subjects.

Many people consider their cats and dogs part of the family. In many households, pets are included in family photographs, they sleep on the bed or in the bedroom, and they provide constant companionship throughout the day. Some pets are talked to like people, and, in a significant number of instances, pets act as "silent" confidants. Animals may be intimate companions to some individuals—especially during adolescence or during later life when people become isolated by the deaths of spouses, relatives, and friends.

Doctors at Johns Hopkins Medical Center in Baltimore, Md., found that patients who recover from severe illnesses who have pets seem to live longer than those who don't. In fact, the numbers speak for themselves: One study showed that 50 out of 53 former patients who had pets were alive a year after their first heart attack; only 17 of the 39 patients who didn't have pets survived the year.

The unconditional love you receive from a cat or dog can do wonders for your mental health, too. Humans are fundamentally social beings. We need to reach out to others, and if there isn't another human around, a pet will do just as nicely.

The ability of animals to connect with humans is the underlying reason behind the companion animal programs that are popping up at nursing homes and various medical institutions around the country. Animals are particularly useful in

Hope, Faith & Healing

helping wheelchair-bound people interact with those around them. Research shows that people with noticeable physical handicaps tend to be avoided or ignored by others—even by people they know. Adding a companion animal to the picture, studies show, increases quality and quantity of attention directed toward the handicapped person.

The loss of a loved animal can have severe negative influences on both our health and mental state, however. There are few support mechanisms for those who have lost a pet,  and there seems to be a general lack of knowledge among friends and family of the seriousness of such a loss. Indeed, individuals who lose their pets may conceal their grief for fear of ridicule or appearing weak.

Many elderly individuals lose their pets, not because of the death of the animal, but because the elderly are often forced out of housing and into nursing homes where pets are not accepted. Having to give up a pet can be a severe source of stress that leads to depression or physical illness, says Katcher. The elderly person who has to give up a pet not only loses the pet's comfort and companionship but is also vulnerable to the severe stress or depression that may follow such a loss.

Not everyone has close relationships with friends, a warm and supportive family, or a friendly pooch to fetch their slippers. Some people have no one to turn to and, as a result, may feel isolated, lonely, or depressed. For these individuals, psychotherapy may be beneficial. No matter what type of therapy is involved, studies have found that the bond that forms between a patient and a counselor can improve emotional and mental states.

One of the reasons psychotherapy might help boost healing, psychologists suspect, is through the fostering of hope. Studies have shown that patients with heart disease live longer and healthier lives when they are given psychotherapy in addition to other treatments. This is because depression, hopelessness, and stress are all related to higher death rates in patients with coronary artery disease.

Not only does therapy nurture hope, but therapy can also improve your attitude. Studies have shown that people with positive attitudes (those who feel comfortable with themselves and who feel they have some control over both the present and the future) almost always heal more quickly than those individuals who feel badly about themselves.

Scientists at Massachusetts General Hospital studied the value of having a psychiatrist visit patients who were recovering from heart attacks. Not surprisingly, those patients who received consultation said they felt better and were less anxious and depressed. They were also more likely to survive their heart attacks.

Psychologists at UCLA found that cancer patients who received supportive and educational home visits had significantly longer survival rates, even when differences in medication were taken into account.

Another UCLA study looked at patients with malignant melanoma (a deadly form of skin cancer) who were assigned to a series of weekly support groups designed to help them cope with the disease. The psychiatrists discovered that the individuals who received therapy and support had better coping strategies and were less depressed than the group that didn't participate in the therapeutic sessions. Six months later, the UCLA team found significant differences in immune system response between the two groups. When they looked at natural killer T cells (the type of white blood cell that kills invading cancer cells), the individuals who had participated in group therapy had more killer-cell activity. Thus, it seemed the im-

Listening and Survival

Being able to talk to someone who listens to you can boost your health, according to one recent study. Patients who were recovering in cancer wards where hospital staff were trained to really listen to them recovered three times faster than patients in other wards.

mune systems of the cancer patients had been strengthened by the group therapy. Even more surprisingly, more than six years later, the patients who had participated in group therapy had

enjoyed substantially longer periods of remission, and fewer of those individuals ultimately died from the skin cancer.

In study after study, scientists find that patients' general health improves after just a few sessions with a mental health expert. Some experts believe that counseling affects physical health because many diseases are "disorders of arousal." Constant high stress levels can lead to high blood pressure, migraines, Raynaud disease, irritable bowel syndrome, even asthma. Psychotherapy can ease stress and help patients take an active part in their own health care.

SELF-HELP GROUPS

Since it's obvious that having someone listen to your problems can make you healthier, it shouldn't be surprising that an entire group of interested listeners—the kind you find in a self-help group—can also boost your health. In fact, this is precisely what scientists recently discovered.

In a recent study of breast cancer patients in California, David Spiegel, M.D., randomly assigned 86 patients to attend either a weekly support group or just routine cancer care. To Spiegel's astonishment, after five years, he discovered that on average, patients who had been in the support group lived twice as long as the women who didn't attend the support group, regardless of how advanced their cancer was when they first joined the group. Moreover, the amount of time a woman spent in the support group was related to how long she survived: The average survival time of those who never went to a session was 26 months. Those who went to between one and 10 sessions survived 36.5 months, and those who went to more than 10 sessions survived 41.5 months.

One reason support groups may work so well is that they are a safe place to express the negative emotions that people may not feel comfortable expressing elsewhere. People participating in support groups can share coping strategies and compare themselves with others. It's a powerful way for people to mobilize their resources and face their diseases with courage.

A self-help group can help you triumph over a feeling of isolation or hopelessness, learn techniques to deal with illness, get the latest information on dealing with medical and insurance communities, and learn how to deal with various treatments and their side effects.

There are a number of things to look for if you're searching for a self-help group. You need to find a group of people with problems similar to your own. You should also look for good leadership; try to find a group that's led by a well-trained professional, whether a nurse, doctor, social worker, or psychologist.

Try to find a group that you feel comfortable with—one that has a supportive atmosphere. You should feel comforted and respected. You might be upset at times, but you should feel that at least you have gotten a new perspective on your problem, a feeling of support, and confidence in your ability to handle a tough situation.

If a group makes you feel judged or offers false promises, look elsewhere. There is more than one way to handle a tough situation. Beware of any group that asks you to kick in large amounts of money. Most self-help groups are free or have only nominal charges to cover expenses.

Where to Find Support

There are plenty of places where you can reach out to find support. Try some of these:

- Church groups
- Political organizations
- Single-parent groups
- Book discussion groups
- Volunteer organizations
- Parenting groups
- Health clubs

Allegiance to family and close friends is important, but for many people, being a part of a larger community, such as a neighborhood, is also essential to well-being. Community life is more than an American dream—it plays a vital role in healing.

Over the past 20 years, many studies have suggested that the social support you find in your community can be vital to your body and your mind, protecting against everything from the common cold to depression. A sense of belonging can help ease the pain of grief, boost the immune system, and inhibit the development of serious disease.

The importance of close family and community ties can be illustrated by the town of Roseto, Pa. Researchers in the mid-1950s to early 1960s found a remarkably low incidence of deaths from heart attack in the close-knit Italian-American community despite risk factors such as lack of exercise, high

Social Support and the Elderly

According to a Yale University study, there are three factors that may help older folks survive illness:

- Having a child who lives within 50 miles
- Believing and participating in religion
- Having at least two good friends

fat intake, obesity, and smoking. At this time, the townspeople of Roseto still embraced "Old World" values such as close family and community ties, a secure and respected place for elders, and a low level of social competitiveness. In 1965, the death rate from heart attacks among people in Roseto was half that of people in the neighboring community of Bangor. But, as traditional family and community ties loosened in Roseto, the death rate from heart attacks slowly began to climb. By 1975, the death rates from heart attacks in this now "Ameri-

canized" and "modern" town had reached the same level as that of Bangor and closely resembled that in the United States at large.

Ironically, Americans are just now discovering how important community is to our health—at a time when many of us feel we are drifting farther away into isolation. One hundred years ago, the average American family included relatives from several generations, all of whom grew up together in the same community. Today, one-fourth of all Americans live alone in separate households.

The movement away from community began in the late 1940s and early 1950s, as Americans began moving from place to place, jumping from job to job, in the hopes of becoming upwardly mobile. Whether for a better job or a bigger house, it was acceptable to move away from family in order to move up. Gradually, the family unit began to unravel and the bonds that once held them together were disrupted.

But experts believe that this trend toward isolation may be slowing down. Co-housing is a way for individuals to fulfill their commitment to community. Co-housing is a Scandinavian concept that exists somewhere between an apartment complex and a commune. It combines private living units with shared community facilities, usually with plenty of open green spaces in between. The majority of co-housing developments in this country are currently found in Washington and California, many of which include gardens, day care, volleyball courts, and a communal dining hall. Co-housing may indeed be the key to reaching out and reconnecting the bonds between ourselves and our communities.

Sometimes it's easy to forget about the resources we have around us. When you're feeling stressed, stop and think about who is out there for you. How big your social network is may well be less important than how you feel about the people you can call on for support. It's the depth of the relationship, not how full your dance card is, that really counts when it comes to your health.

CHAPTER 5
Alternative Healing

Today stress may well be at an all-time high. In an age of corporate downsizing and rising medical costs, we worry about keeping our jobs—and our health. More than ever before, we need successful ways to relax, to bring stress-free time into our busy lives.

Stress is defined as a physical, chemical, or emotional factor that causes bodily or mental tension. When we are stressed, our pituitary and adrenal glands release chemicals, such as adrenaline and cortisol, that instruct the body to initiate what is called a *fight or flight* sequence. Our heart rates rise, our blood pressures increase, our pupils dilate, we perspire, and we feel a rush of strength, the so-called *adrenaline rush*.

This rush of adrenaline can be beneficial when we have a challenge to meet, such as a race to win or an exciting project at work. But when the pressure is unrelenting, we remain in a constant state of stress, which is unhealthy.

Soon our bodies and minds begin to react negatively. We develop headaches, stiff necks, nagging backaches, sweaty palms, upset stomachs, and a slew of other aches and pains. Normally patient and understanding, we become irritable, our tempers on a short fuse. Our energy levels are low, we can't concentrate, and we jump at the slightest interruption.

When we suffer from too much stress, we can't organize our thoughts well, our creativity is hampered, and our learning ability is inhibited. At this point we need to recognize and deal with our high level of stress, before we develop dangerous health conditions such as heart disease, lung disease, and high blood pressure.

We can combat our life-threatening stress in a variety of ways, including alternative therapies. Some of these therapies are ancient: Meditation and yoga have been in existence for thousands of years. Other methods, such as syntonics, are of more recent origin. The key to these types of therapies is the interaction between mind and body.

Unlike conventional medicine, which focuses only on the body, these alternative therapies are based on the concept that both mind and body are connected, that each is an integral part of the treatment program. And, to a patient or physician searching for a new way of dealing with a problematic illness, alternative techniques have much to offer.

The following alternative healing methods can help you cope with—and even recover from—physical, mental, or emotional problems. Whatever the stresses in your life, be they long lines or illness, you are sure to find a technique here that will help you adjust to and take charge of the challenges life sends your way.

Modern physicians are beginning to learn what healers of the past have always known: Plant essences and the scents they produce can be powerful medicine.

Smell is perhaps our most primitive sense, and it is 10,000 times more sensitive than any of our other four senses. It is the only sense that is directly connected to our midbrain area, called the *limbic system*. The limbic system is where sensory experiences—including memory, emotions, sex drive, and hunger—are processed. At one time, the sense of smell helped humans to survive—certain odors alerted us to prowling predators or aroused desire for a mate at a propitious time of the month. These days, however, we tend to take little conscious advantage of our sense of smell. We even do our darndest to mask many of the human scents that served as vital messages to our ancestors.

Our nasal cavities contain mucous membranes that are lined with olfactory cells. As these cells respond to various odors, they send impulses along the olfactory nerve to the limbic system. This direct connection invokes instant reactions. The briefest whiff of a familiar scent enables the limbic system to instantly recall a long-lost memory: The scent of vanilla may remind you of the first time you helped your mother bake sugar cookies. The human brain can process and store as many as 100,000 different smells.

Not surprisingly, the sense of smell has been used in healing rituals for thousands of years. The ceremonial use of smoke and incense has been documented in the religions of many civilizations. Perhaps our ancestors observed that the smoke produced by burning certain bushes or trees produced positive physical effects or even mystical visions.

On a basic level, pleasing aromas are spirit-lifters. But scent was also used in therapeutic ways. The Hindu scriptures of India, the *Vedas*, included passages regarding the use of aromatics for religious rituals, for healing, and purely for pleasure. Temples were built of sandalwood to enhance the spiritual experience. Babylonian and Arab civilizations also

The Nose Knows

Although odors are less important to us than they were to our ancestors, we still use our noses in many ways. They alert us to cakes burning in the oven, leaking gas from a defective pipe, and even the smell of fear—excess perspiration. Studies have shown that women tend to have more sensitive noses than men, thanks to unusually alert scent receptors in the brain. It is speculated that this gender difference is a result of thousands of generations of natural selection for mothers who can tell by smell that their babies are ill or need to be cleaned. Of course, it is impossible to know whether this is actually the cause, but pregnant women and new mothers often report an increased sense of smell.

used scents in the building of their temples and mosques, mixing them with the mortar they used to cement the structures. The Egyptians, however, were the masters of aromatherapy. Combinations of spices were used to preserve bodies in the mummification process. Egyptian priests, astrologers, and doctors used perfumed oils, pungent vinegars, and aromatic resins such as myrrh and frankincense in their rituals and

treatments for illnesses such as mania and depression. With the power of scent, healers found that they could induce relaxation, excite emotions, and heighten the senses.

For many centuries, skilled healers continued to use the aromatic essences of plants. The Greeks and Romans made use of the principles of aromatherapy, and it was the Greeks who first used olive oil as a base for collecting the scent from flower petals. We can thank Arab civilization for the distillation process of extracting plant essences. After the fall of Roman civilization, however, the idea of using plant essences for medicinal purposes was lost or discarded. Herbal healing had a brief revival in Europe after the Crusaders brought knowledge of it back from the Middle East, but its practice became suspect during the witch-hunts of the seventeenth century. The development of modern medicine and pharmaceuticals in the nineteenth century again pushed aromatherapy to the sidelines.

The rebirth of aromatherapy began in France in the early twentieth century. Aromatherapy, which is not limited to scent, is described as the medicinal use of plant compounds, such as flowers, seeds, leaves, stems, bark, and roots. The term was coined by a French chemist, R. M. Gattefosse, who became interested in the healing powers of plants after a severe burn to his hand was helped when he accidentally plunged it into lavender oil. He investigated the healing properties of essential oils and found that they had many uses. Certain oils could fight bacteria and viruses and reduce inflammation; others had a disinfectant effect. (Herbs such as oregano, savory, and thyme have antiseptic properties because of their high phenol content.) Dr. Gattefosse wrote about his discoveries, and the use of aromatherapy and phytotherapy (herbal medicine) gained credence in Europe.

Essential oils are believed to provide relief from a number of common ailments. Essential oils are chemically complex—containing hormonelike properties, vitamins and minerals, and natural antiseptics. The chemical components of various plants may have enormous healing potentials—they may be capable of enhancing immunity, lessening pain, inducing relaxation, fighting fungal infections, relieving the symptoms of premenstrual syndrome, and softening skin.

The powers of essential oils are dependent on their purity and quality. To produce even a tiny amount of an essential oil, great quantities of botanicals are necessary, and it is not always easy to find natural oils that have not been adulterated. For clinical purposes, synthetic oils cannot be substituted. "Only the natural, living plant extract carries the healing potential," says Peter Holmes, who is a doctor of Oriental medicine and a clinical aromatherapist at the Artemis Institute of Natural Therapies in Boulder, Colorado. Synthetic oils will not heal infections. With practice, you can rely on your nose to alert you to the difference between a high-quality natural oil and one that is synthetic or adulterated. (If you're having trouble determining the difference, check the product label.)

It is through therapeutic massage that clinical aromatherapy has become most widespread. But health care practitioners such as acupuncturists, nurses, occupational therapists, and counselors are also finding that aromatherapy enhances their treatments. Aromatherapy, which in France is described as "soft medicine," works more slowly than conventional medications, but used properly it can have a direct and beneficial effect on certain health problems, whether they originate in the body or the psyche. The physiologically stimulating or relaxing effect of some essential oils makes them useful in treating muscular or arthritic conditions. Aromatherapy can also play a role in reducing the effects of stress and depression. "Because of the nature of essential oils, clinical aromatherapy's working method is essentially nondualistic, addressing the individual's body and mind as a whole," Holmes says. "Where the origin of disease is in the psyche, the oils as fragrance will work through the neuroendocrine functions down to the physical body to heal and re-establish harmony. Where the origin of disease is in the body, it will work through the body's physiology up to the mental and emotional levels to heal and harmonize the whole person."

Certain essential oils, including basil, lavender, marjoram, orange, and ylang-ylang, have relaxing properties. Used in conjunction with a warm or hot bath, these oils can help relieve the effects of stress, such as headaches and sleeplessness. Drinking an herbal tea containing orange blossom or mint can be calming before bedtime. Marjoram, mint, thyme, and verbena are good tea choices if you're looking for an energy boost. If you are depressed, a salad containing marjoram and thyme may lift your spirits; the scent of these herbs can have a cheering or energizing effect.

Peppermint oil and eucalyptus oil are used in a variety of traditional treatments for pain, including headaches. A German study found that a preparation of peppermint and eucalyptus oil applied to the forehead and temples significantly reduced tension in the temporal muscle of the head. The study of 32 healthy men found that this combination did not reduce sensitivity to pain, however, but a combination of peppermint and ethanol did.

Aromatherapy also may be very helpful for people who wish to quit smoking. A North Carolina study of cigarette smokers found that those who puffed on a device that delivered a vapor from essential oil of black pepper had significantly reduced cravings for cigarettes. Persons who inhaled the vapors from the pepper also had reduced emotional and physical symptoms of anxiety compared with a control group.

Part of the practice of aromatherapy involves knowing how to mix essential oils to produce the most beneficial effects as well as the best ways to apply them. Most clinical aromatherapy involves the physiological use of essential oils to stimulate or relax the body or to fight infection. In addition to being inhaled—either directly or through facial saunas—essential oils can be applied topically in conjunction with a massage or added to a warm bath. The combined effect of touch and fragrance is extremely soothing. The porous nature of the skin ensures the oil's effectiveness; you might even say that the skin "breathes" in the oil, just as the nose breathes in its aroma. Bases with which essential oils can be mixed for massage include almond, soy, and wheat germ oils.

Sexy Scents

Did you know that certain aromas can enhance your sex life? Essential oils such as cedarwood, rose, ylang-ylang, clove, and ginger have reputations as sexual stimulants or aphrodisiacs. Cinnamon, too, has a sexy reputation that belies its homey image. It was once used to scent linens before lovemaking, and in a recent study, male participants exposed to the aroma of just-baked cinnamon buns consistently got erections.

Poultices or compresses can also be used to apply essential oils or herbs. An herb's seeds or leaves can be prepared as teas or used in cooking.

Essential oils and botanicals can also have a beneficial effect when diffused into the environment. In a clinical setting, Holmes says, essential oils can be used to promote aseptic conditions, gently energize the staff, and relax and support the patients. At Memorial Sloan-Kettering Cancer Center in New York City, the vanilla-almond fragrance of heliotropine was found to allay the anxieties of patients about to undergo magnetic resonance imaging, a medical procedure that requires them to remain still while enclosed in a long tube. Future studies are likely to confirm the importance of aromatherapy in easing patient anxiety.

Room sprays and lightbulb diffusers are other ways of using the pleasing aromas of essential oils, although these sorts of

Hope, Faith & Healing

air fresheners do not necessarily serve a therapeutic purpose. Savvy travelers often use these products to scent a hotel room to ensure a good night's rest.

Fragrance has also been found to improve performance in the workplace, increasing productivity, efficiency, and compatibility among coworkers. The sweet, refreshing fragrances of peppermint, lily of the valley, lavender, jasmine, and lemon are especially suited for this purpose. Not surprisingly, businesses in Japan—a country known for its emphasis on productivity and hard work—have begun to take advantage of this knowledge. A company called Shimizu Technology Center America has sold its fragrance-emitting system—which releases bursts of scent through ventilation ducts—to many Japanese banks, hotels, nursing homes, and offices.

Although aromatherapy may seem like a safe, simple form of treatment, it's important to realize that plant extracts are powerful. Just because something is natural does not mean it is safe. Essential oils are effective in tiny amounts; indeed, they can be harmful if used undiluted or taken internally, especially by people who are elderly, very young, pregnant, or ill. Plant essences should always be administered in small amounts at the proper dilution, especially when applied to the skin.

Aromatherapy is not always an ideal form of treatment. Pregnant women may react adversely to certain scents because of the hormonal changes in their bodies. Of even greater concern, research suggests, is that some essential oils may have the power to induce miscarriages. For these reasons, aromatherapy should not be used during pregnancy. People with sensitive skin or those who have frequent allergic reactions, asthma, cancer, epilepsy, heart conditions, or high blood pressure also should avoid using essential oils.

As the twentieth century comes to a close, we are finding that technology alone does not have all the answers. The growing success of aromatherapy shows us that the road to good health sometimes means taking alternative routes, or simply following our noses. If you're interested in pursuing aromatherapy as an alternative healing technique, a reputable aromatherapist can help get you started.

MUSIC THERAPY

Music is an innate part of the human condition. Even before birth, music is a part of our lives. We sense the rhythmic beat of our mother's heart, the rise and fall of her breathing, the gurglings of her stomach as it digests the food that will nourish us. Music brings back memories, moves us to action, and soothes our aching spirits.

The early beginnings of music, art, and dance testify to people's inborn need to express themselves creatively. When our species developed language, song was not far behind. Then we created other ways to make music. To make our first musical instruments, we hollowed out bones or reeds and blew into them. It probably was not long thereafter that we made drums

by stretching skins over hollow gourds. In the land once known as Mesopotamia, the cradle of civilization, archaeologists have found evidence of instruments such as pipes, drums, triangles, and stringed instruments that date to 3500 B.C. Bamboo pipes are mentioned in Chinese texts dating to about 2700 B.C.

Early societies ascribed a magic origin to sound and music. How else could one explain the power that it seemed to wield? It was a widespread belief that music could drive out evil spirits that caused madness or illness. Around the world, ancient peoples—and some tribal societies today—used chants, prayers, incantations, affirmations, and holy words in their musical rituals.

Researchers have found that music can affect heart rate, breathing, and stomach contractions. Recent studies show that music played before or after surgery can reduce anxiety and decrease the amount of anesthesia a patient requires. Quiet music has been shown to reduce physiological responses to stress by lowering the body's heart rate, blood pressure, and respiration rate, and to increase the tolerance of pain. (Research shows that premature babies grow faster and go home sooner when they are lulled to sleep by the sweet sounds of

Brahms's lullaby.) In addition, sounds that are repeated hypnotically, such as humming or the chanting of mantras, have proven to be helpful in treating irregular heart rhythms.

The brain's right frontal region is responsible for musical ability and perception of music; this area is also associated with emotion. According to the findings of a University of Michigan researcher, slow music in minor keys "warms" the brain, fostering alertness and arousal of the limbic system, where our emotions are housed. Upbeat music in major keys puts us in a good mood. Music with a high pitch also tends to have a positive effect on our emotions.

When uplifting music is joined with uplifting words—as in the case of a joyous hymn or national anthem—powerful emotions are stirred. Thus, music has become an important part of all of our major life ceremonies, many of which have a liturgical basis—worship, weddings, wakes. Indeed, music and religion have an integral relationship. The ritual of making or hearing music, especially in a religious or celebratory context, allows us to express emotions that would otherwise be restricted by the limitations of words.

Music affects us physically, too. When the beat is right, we clap our hands, tap our toes, wiggle our hips, snap our fingers, and sway to the sound. As we sing or listen to music that we enjoy, our pupils grow large, and painkilling endorphins flood our bodies, giving us a thrill of pleasure. Tunes that are easygoing or repetitive have a relaxing effect, sending us right

Hearing 101

Even the action of hearing is rhythmic. When a sound is made, the outer ear captures the sound waves, directing them down the auditory canal to the eardrum. The sound waves then bounce from the eardrum to three tiny bones: the hammer, the anvil, and the stirrup. From there the waves pass on to the fluid-filled inner ear where they reverberate against the snail-shaped cochlea, which is lined with tiny hairs that vibrate. These vibrations stimulate the auditory nerve cells, which relay the information to the brain, where the sound is interpreted.

into dreamland. Lullabies, for instance, have a beat that is unrelenting. Upbeat music energizes us, which is why we like to exercise or dance to it. The type of music most likely to rouse us to action is made up of variations on the familiar; it's neither too monotonous nor too offbeat. We respond to percussive, or tapping, rhythms that vary in their patterns. We are likely to ignore music to which we can't keep a beat.

Music therapy is defined as the creative use of music in a clinical setting to establish an interaction, a shared musical experience, and activity. Its goal is to help people restore, maintain, or improve their mental and physical health by aiding their physical, psychological, and emotional integration.

Modern music therapy evolved as a consequence of war. In an effort to entertain and comfort the veterans of World War II, musicians of all stripes took their talents to the veterans' hospitals around the country. To the surprise of the attending doctors and nurses, the music had a profoundly positive effect on their patients' health and behavior. It was felt that musicians with the proper training could provide even greater benefits. In 1944, Michigan State University offered the world's first music therapy degree program; today, there are music therapy programs at 65 colleges. In 1950, the National Association for Music Therapy (NAMT) was founded. Today it counts more than 5,000 music therapists among its members.

Music therapy's applications are universal: People of all ages can benefit from music therapy, whether or not they have any musical ability, and all types of music—from classical to jazz to rock and roll—can offer therapeutic value. The only caveat is that in order for music to work its magic, it must be music that we enjoy. (Playing rap music for a senior citizen who grew up listening to Glenn Miller, for example, is more likely to have a negative than a positive effect.)

With the help of music, people can make positive changes in their behavior as well as share their thoughts and feelings in a safe environment. (You may have noticed how much easier it is to carry on a conversation at a party if there's music in the background.) Music can give patients a more positive outlook and a more cooperative attitude. Therapists and physicians have found that music's power lies not only in its emotional or motivational value but also in its neurological effects.

Participation in music pays off in unique sensory experiences. These experiences range from barely perceptible responses on the neuromuscular level to the highest level of human behavior—intellectual meditation and contemplation—all of which are essential to the aesthetic experience. The multiple stimuli involved in music are aural (musical and verbal), visual (musical notation and conductor cues), and tactile (the actual feel of an instrument). It's this integration of sensory, motor, emotional, and social components that give music its amazing power. Additionally, the making of music can be as simple as singing a rhyme or as complex as composing a symphony. Capability, mood, motivation, intellect, and level of musical knowledge all determine how music can be used.

Whether a therapist uses speech or song or merely the act of listening to music, these methods can be potent tools in opening up lines of communication and strengthening social interaction with both children and adults. Through their choice of music or the way they play music, people can express negative feelings, energetic behavior, or feelings of closeness that they might otherwise find impossible to share in a socially acceptable way. The goal of music therapy is to help people move from random or uncontrolled expression to organized, meaningful expression of their emotions.

The structured form of music demands preciseness, another reason it is useful in therapy. For instance, children who are mentally retarded or autistic often find comfort in rhythm, order, and repetition, so they respond well to music therapy. By using movement, rhythm, sounds, language, and musical expression in a group setting, therapists teach tasks step by step, with simple chants, rondos, and poems providing structure. Setting the information to music makes it easier for children to learn and remember. (If you've ever had an advertising jingle stuck in your head, you know how true this is.) And specially designed percussive instruments allow all children to participate, no matter what their ability.

"Almost all children respond to music," says Clive Robbins, a certified music therapist at the New York University Nordoff-Robbins Center for Music Therapy, which helps handicapped children learn, relate to, and communicate with others. According to the National Association for Music Therapy Web site, says Robbins: "Music is an open-sesame, and if you can use it carefully and appropriately, you can reach into that child's potential for development."

By its very nature, music brings people together, and among the tools used by music therapists are patient choirs and musical skills groups. In a world in which people who are different are frequently ignored, laughed at, or pitied, the challenge of a physical, mental, or emotional handicap can be overwhelming. Participation in a choir or other musical group brings feelings of acceptance that may be lacking for these individuals. Instead of rejection, the experience is one not only of belonging but also of accomplishment, gratification, mastery, even normalcy. The result can be a healthy acceptance of limitations and the realization that inability in one area does not mean inability in all aspects of life. For some people, this insight is a breakthrough that can make an amazing difference in their lifelong expectations.

Another valuable aspect of music therapy is its emphasis on teamwork, especially in institutional settings. To bring about the common goal of beautiful music, an individual member of a musical group must learn to relate well to his peers as well as subordinate his desires and interests to those of the group. The goals of this type of therapy are to gradually increase the size of the group in which an individual can successfully interact, increase the range and flexibility of his behavior in those interactions, and provide experiences that will help him better relate to noninstitutional life.

With music, therapists can teach concepts such as direction, numbers, and letters. If you've ever known a child who learned his alphabet or counting skills by watching children's television shows such as *Sesame Street*, you know how well this combination of music and learning works. Other concepts or skills that can be taught with the aid of music therapy include body image and awareness, spatial relationships, simple categorizing, and simple association.

With any form of therapy, communication is the key. Music therapy may often bring about certain ideas or images. If these ideas fall outside a range considered to be normal, the differences can help the therapist understand how clients perceive or structure their world. The associations stimulated by the music can then be used to reinforce more acceptable ideas or behaviors. Often, this type of therapy is used with psychiatric patients, teenagers, or geriatric patients.

Other psychosocial benefits of music therapy include the building of self-esteem and motivational skills. Through structured musical situations, therapists can help their clients experience various levels of success and a sense of belonging. In addition to the pleasure inherent in performing music, people learn through their own efforts the relationship between effort and accomplishment. The truth of the adage "practice makes perfect" is never more clear than when it is applied to the making of music. And while the making of music is often its own reward, it doesn't hurt that talented musicians are applauded and praised by those who hear them. For a child or adult who has suffered emotional abuse, for instance, the glowing feeling of accomplishment after a successful performance can be one of the most important steps on the road to renewed self-esteem.

Music is also a socially acceptable way in which people can compete with others, especially if they are physically chal-

lenged in some way. And the commitment of time music requires can have a motivational aspect. After all, it's impossible
to play or sing only one note a day. The commitment of time
is especially important in a group situation, in which members must rely on each other not only to show up for rehearsal
but also to show up on time. The acceptance of responsibility
this entails contributes to personal growth, further enhancing
the therapeutic effect of music therapy.

Another type of music therapy involves guided imagery, a
technique that makes use of the relaxing effects of classical
music to encourage the
visualization of benefi-
cial images (see page
225). With mind and
body relaxed by the
music, the client reflects
on the images evoked by
the sound. With the help
of the therapist, the
client explores the im-
ages and their meanings.

Rather than being a way of curing or treating symptoms,
guided imagery with music is an attempt to understand and
solve problems by seeking inner awareness.

Music therapy offers physical benefits as well. Many hospitals have learned that music lessens pain when used in con-

junction with anesthesia or pain medication; elevates patients' moods and counteracts depression; and acts as a sedative, helping to induce sleep or counteract fear or apprehension. From surgical suites to intensive care units to the delivery rooms where women give birth, music has found an important place in hospital care. Applications for music therapy are constantly expanding as new benefits are reported from many different medical specialties and disciplines.

Medical procedures can be difficult for any number of reasons, including patient anxiety. Several studies have examined music therapy's ability to lessen both the anxiety and the sensation of pain involved in some medical procedures. A study of 38 adults who arrived in the emergency room with cuts large enough to require stitches were randomly assigned to undergo the procedure with or without music. The group with music reported significantly less pain during the procedure, according to an article published in the *Annals of Emergency Medicine* in 1991.

At St. Agnes Hospital in Baltimore, Maryland, classical music was piped into critical care units. A half hour of music was found to be equivalent to 10 milligrams of Valium. At some hospitals, patients being prepped for surgery are fitted with earphones playing classical music. One woman, brought to St. Luke's Hospital in Cleveland, Ohio, after she had been seriously injured in a car accident, remained calm before surgery and required less sedation, thanks to the sounds of Vivaldi's "Four Seasons." The Brahms and Mozart piped into the surgical suite helped keep her surgical team relaxed. The woman continued to listen to soothing music after returning home and found that the painkillers her doctors had prescribed weren't necessary.

Even the pain of childbirth can be lessened with the right music. In one study of about 30 deliveries, half the women who listened to music didn't require anesthesia. In some delivery rooms, relaxing music is played for the first phase of delivery, when a woman needs to conserve her strength. When birth is imminent and more energy is required to push the baby through the birth canal, the music's tempo is increased.

Studies have shown that people with varying degrees of depressive disorder may also benefit greatly from music therapy. One study, published in the *Journal of the American Medical Association* in 1995, examined the effect of music therapy on 30 older adults diagnosed with depressive disorder. The study showed that those assigned to the treatment group who underwent at-home music therapy on a weekly basis reported less distress, a better mood, and more self-esteem than the untreated control group.

According to an article published in the *Journal of Holistic Nursing* in 1995, listening to music before bed can have a relaxing effect on both body and mind. The study of music therapy in 25 elderly adults with sleep disturbances revealed that music therapy improved sleep patterns in 24 of the subjects.

An experiment by Deforia Lane, Ph.D., at Rainbow Babies and Childrens Hospital in Kansas City, Kansas, showed just how important the sense of hearing can be. Lane, who specializes in physical and psychological rehabilitation of cancer patients, found that the body's level of salivary IgA—an immunoglobulin the body uses to accelerate recovery, reduce the likelihood of infection, and control the heart rate—increased after a 30-minute session of music therapy. She reported her findings in Oncology Nursing Forum and Journal of Oncology Management.

And music does not discriminate by age. For example, studies of premature and low-birth-weight babies at the UCLA School of Nursing and Atlanta's Georgia Baptist Medical Center determined that the infants gained weight more quickly and made more efficient use of oxygen when exposed to music combined with the sounds of voices.

In nursing homes, music helps stimulate memory and movement. A favorite song of long ago can bring back pleasant memories and help initiate conversation. Patients with Alzheimer disease who may remember nothing else are often reoriented by the sound of music.

Physical fitness is another benefit of music in nursing homes, where it can be difficult to help patients maintain quality of life and keep physically fit. But gentle exercise to music helps reduce pain and keeps the residents moving for a longer period of time. And, according to research at the Colorado State University Center for Biomedical Research in Music, stroke victims who exercised to music showed an improved ability to walk.

Even for healthy people, music is a vital support for physical exercise. How many fitness routines are you aware of that *aren't* set to music? How many gyms have you been to where people practice aerobic routines in silence? Whether you're a teenager or a golden-ager, music encourages frequency of exercise.

At present, research into music's therapeutic value consists mainly of single case studies, occasional reports on small groups, and anecdotal reports, but the future of music therapy is promising. With new research into its effectiveness for physical rehabilitation and therapy for patients with Alzheimer disease, music therapists hope to more thoroughly document music's value. It's only natural that people throughout the ages will continue to turn to music when they need to be healed.

ART THERAPY

Art was perhaps the earliest form of creative expression, and the early shamans, or tribal spiritual leaders, were among our first artists. The art they created had ritualistic significance, depicting the needs of the community—more food, spiritual contact, or better health. Today, in societies such as the Basotho of South Africa, women paint murals on the outer walls of their homes that represent the community's hope for a fertile crop year. If their wish is granted, the spring rains come, washing away the murals; new ones are then painted on the outer walls the following year.

Even for our earliest ancestors, the healing process was a complex ritual that often involved some form of music, dance, or art. But the use of art in healing was not limited to these ancient societies. Priests in the Ethiopian Orthodox Church used art in the form of parchment scrolls that featured bold graphics and lettering to heal. The scrolls, which date to the sixteenth century, are a form of preventive and curative medicine in some African communities when they're hung before a sick person. The content of the scrolls include references to ancient cultural and religious beliefs. Sculptures, masks, and amulets are other forms of art that have been used to heal.

The link between art and healing continued into the early twentieth century, when psychiatrists began studying art created by their patients. Swiss psychiatrist Carl Jung, the founder of analytic psychology, believed that the realm of the unconscious could be represented through images and symbols in art, dance,

music, poetry, and other forms of creative expression. During the same period, it was discovered that the art of children, with its spontaneity and naturalness, represented communication that was both emotional and symbolic in nature. According to the American Art Therapy Association, in the 1930s, art therapy emerged as a distinct profession.

Today, art therapy is used in education and medicine to help people with developmental, social, psychological, or health problems. From couples in counseling to children who have been emotionally or physically abused, art can play a role in healing. Among the institutions that may have an art therapist on staff are halfway houses, medical or psychiatric hospitals, nursing homes, pain clinics, prisons, residential treatment centers, schools, shelters, and universities.

Art therapy can be useful in working with children, adolescents, and adults who have repressed traumatic memories. According to a 1992 article in the *Journal of Psychosocial Nursing and Mental Health Services*, in instances of sexual abuse, art therapy can help children and adolescents to overcome resistance, build trust, reduce tension, and stimulate memory.

Veterans suffering from post-traumatic stress disorder have been found to benefit from art therapy as well. According to a 1993 article in the *Journal of Psychosocial Nursing and Mental Health Services*, art therapy seeks to help these individuals improve their coping patterns through individual and group interventions that promote expression of thoughts and feelings, congruency between experience and self-concept, and feelings of effectiveness in behavior modification.

Studies have shown that people with AIDS, arthritis, cancer, and heart disease have also found art therapy to be beneficial. Art therapy is frequently used as a counseling tool for people facing serious or life-threatening diseases or aggressive medical treatments. Because each case is different, the therapist tailors his or her approach to the patient's needs, based on the illness, medications, or treatment protocol involved.

Working in tandem with physicians, psychologists, nurses, rehabilitation counselors, social workers, and teachers, art therapists use their knowledge of developmental and psychological theories to assess and treat a client's needs, based on his or her responses to images, the creative process, and the artistic results of that process. The therapist interprets the art, studying such elements as distortion of shapes, missing items or people, centrality of objects, color, placement of barriers, unusual representations, perspective, and shading to help identify what is going on in the client's psyche.

In its simplest aspect, art gives pleasure, but it is also psychologically restorative because it allows us to explore our feelings or reveal our experiences without expressing them verbally, something that, for some people, can be difficult or frightening. When we feel that our lives are spiraling out of control, art gives us a way to express how we feel. In that creative process, we find release, in much the same way that meditation brings release, because of the total absorption it requires. By focusing on art instead of on our pain or problems, we become better able to relax, to put our energies to positive ends rather than negative ones. Through art, we learn to connect with our inner self, growing spiritually, emotionally, and psychologically. The transformation affects our attitude, or viewpoint, bringing into play the powerful mind-body link.

Masterpieces are produced by great artists; in art therapy, style is not important—only artistic expression matters, not execution. And yet therapeutic art often receives public recognition in galleries and museums. One artist, Thelma Wasserman-Friedman, is a survivor of breast cancer. Her work was exhibited at the Milwaukee Art Museum under the title "Confronting Cancer Through Art." At New York's Memorial Sloan-Kettering Cancer Center, there are frequent exhibits of the art created by patients, who find that the creative process helps to carry them through the pains and fears of diagnosis and treatment.

DANCE THERAPY

Body language is one of the most basic forms of communication. Dancing has been used for centuries to express emotion, often in a ritualistic or ceremonial nature. People danced to celebrate birth or victory in battle, to bring rain or otherwise summon the powers of nature, or to drive away evil spirits. Dance has long been a form of storytelling; it uses the body

The Benefits of Dance

Although extensive studies of dance therapy have not been conducted, it has been widely used in clinical practice for a variety of purposes:

• ameliorating depression

• decreasing fear and anxiety

• decreasing isolation

• decreasing bodily tension

• developing body image

• enhancing circulatory and respiratory function

• expressing anger

• facilitating attention

• increasing communication skills

• increasing feelings of well-being

• increasing and expanding self-concept and self-esteem

• increasing verbalization

• promoting healing

• reducing chronic pain

• reducing suicidal thoughts

to give meaning to movement. Dance is a direct expression of the mind and body and can therefore be a powerful tool for healing and therapy.

Cultures throughout the world have used dance as a way to bond communities, celebrate events, pray to higher powers, and heal the sick. The modern beginning of dance as a healing therapy can be traced to the 1940s when psychiatrists in Washington, D.C., showed that their patients were deriving therapeutic benefits from attending dance classes led by Marian Chase. Considered a pioneer of dance therapy in the United States, Chase was asked to work with psychiatric patients considered too disturbed to participate in group activities.

By definition, dance therapy is the psychotherapeutic use of movement to further an individual's physical, mental, and emotional integration. In this form of therapy, movement is the agent of change, reconnecting the link between mind and body through both verbal and nonverbal expression. As with art and music therapy, it is the nonverbal nature of dance that makes it so powerful.

United and energized by rhythm, not words, dance permits us to communicate and to expose our feelings, which helps to bring about change in the way we think, feel, and act, both emotionally and physically.  Dance therapy is typically used for people with cognitive, emotional, and/or social problems. It seeks to help emotionally disturbed patients express their feelings, gain insight, and develop healthy attachments.

Elderly persons can use dance therapy to enhance vitality, express fear and grief, develop relationships, and maintain a healthy body. Physically disabled persons can benefit from dance therapy as a way to help increase movement and self-esteem, have fun, and heighten creativity. And mentally retarded persons can use dance therapy to help develop better social skills, increase body awareness, and motivate learning.

Dance therapists work with people of all ages individually or in group settings. Therapists work in settings such as adult day-care centers, clinics, community mental health centers, correctional facilities, general and psychiatric hospitals, infant development centers, private practice, and schools and recreational facilities.

Dance therapy is believed to help reduce anxiety. A study of 84 college students compared anxiety before and after three months of dance class with students enrolled in exercise, music, and mathematical classes. The study, which appeared in a 1990 issue of *American Journal of Dance Therapy*, found that students in the dance class had significantly lower levels of anxiety, but that students in the other groups had no significant reduction in anxiety.

In recent years, dance therapy has been used for disease prevention and health promotion among healthy people, and as a way to reduce stress in persons with AIDS, Alzheimer disease, and cancer, as well as individuals who care for them.

For more information on dance therapy, visit your local library or bookstore.

Priests and physicians in ancient Greece, Egypt, China, and India used various colors in their healing rituals. Ancient teachings of India separate the body into seven energy centers, called *chakras;* a different color is associated with each chakra. In medieval Europe, red hangings around a bed were thought to prevent scarring caused by smallpox.

Color permeates our language and culture, almost always evoking an emotional response. We sing the blues when we're sad, see red when we're mad, and become green with envy.

Two areas of the brain are involved in how we perceive color: the cortex and the midbrain. Certain areas of our brains—the hypothalamus and the pituitary and pineal glands—are highly sensitive to light. Since color is light of different wavelengths, it is not surprising that different colors can affect us physiologically and psychologically. For instance, color has been shown to increase or decrease blood pressure, pulse rate, and respiration rate. (The color yellow brought on the highest increases in blood pressure and pulse and respiration rates; black brought the greatest decreases.)

Sitting Pretty

In your mind, is prison a dark, forbidding place? Well, thanks to several studies performed in the 1980s, prison life is about to lighten up. Bubble-gum pink is no longer the sole province of little girls' rooms and beauty parlors. Because the color was found to reduce the incidence of violent behavior, now many jails and prisons have pink holding cells.

Clinical psychologist Alexander Schauss of Tacoma, Washington, was the first to advocate using pink to quiet aggression. The color, known as Baker-Miller pink, has been shown to physically reduce aggressive behavior within minutes, thus decreasing the need to restrain inmates with force or sedative medications. Schauss' research has been reported in The Journal of Orthomolecular Psychiatry, the Bulletin of The Psychonomic Society, and the International Journal of Biosocial Research.

In a University of Texas study, researchers measured the hand-grip strength of participants while they watched displays of colored lights. The strength of their grips increased by 13.5 percent when they saw red, a color that has been found to stimulate the brain in previous studies. Other studies have shown the relaxing effect the color blue has on the brain.

Therapeutically, color has been used to treat babies with jaundice, people with rheumatoid arthritis, and sufferers of migraine headaches. Neonatal jaundice, which commonly affects babies born prematurely, results when skin and body tissues have too high an accumulation of bilirubin, a chemical that turns the skin yellow. It has been found that blue light breaks up bilirubin, making it easier for the body to eliminate it.

Blue light may also have the ability to reduce pain. A 1982 study at San Diego State University School of Nursing showed that the same amount of blue light used for jaundiced babies could significantly lessen the pain of arthritis. When blue light was directed for up to 15 minutes toward the hands of 60 women with rheumatoid arthritis, many of them reported a decrease in the amount of pain they felt.

While it seems paradoxical, a study reported in the January 1990 issue of *Brain/Mind Bulletin* showed that blinking red lights ended migraine headaches within one hour in 72 percent of the participants. Of the 28 percent whose headaches did not cease, 93 percent reported a reduction in pain.

People have long benefited from the applied use of color. With sophisticated diagnostic equipment and techniques, combined with a better understanding of the brain, we may soon discover even more ways that color affects the mind and body.

HUMOR THERAPY

It is often said that laughter is the best medicine. Norman Cousins described his dramatic recovery from illness in his book, *Anatomy of an Illness*: "I made the joyous discovery that ten minutes of genuine belly laughter had an anesthetic effect and would give me at least two hours of pain-free sleep." Cousins used laughter, vitamin C, and a positive attitude to recover from a debilitating illness (ankylosing spondylitis) and resume a full life.

Humor can affect your health on many levels. It can reduce or eliminate stress, ease discomfort, and generally stimulate the mind and body, producing a positive outlook and a healthy perspective. Laughter can increase the production of endorphins— chemicals that act as natural opiates—reducing pain and improving mood. Laughter also increases heart rate and improves circulation. There is evidence that laugher may

even temporarily increase the amount of immunoglobulin A in saliva, a substance that can help fight the initial stages of infections such as the flu and the common cold.

HORTICULTURE THERAPY

As anyone who likes to putter around in the garden or in the backyard can tell you, sometimes just putting your fingers in the dirt or tending to a plant can help relieve stress and make you feel a little more grounded. Horticulture therapy uses this basic feeling in a variety of ways to promote continued health and well-being.

Horticultural therapy uses plants and horticultural activities to improve your social, educational, psychological, and physical adjustment, and thereby improve your body, mind, and spirit. Horticultural therapy involves the patient in all phases of gardening and, sometimes, even in the activity of selling the produce and plants grown.

Horticultural therapy can be beneficial for a wide variety of people, including people who are

- developmentally disabled
- elderly
- mentally ill
- physically disabled
- public offenders
- substance abusers

The first known greenhouse for individuals with mental illnesses was built in 1879 by Pennsylvania Friends Asylum for the Insane (today known as Friends Hospital). Modern day horticultural therapy was fueled in part by its use in rehabilitating disabled veterans of World War II. The first undergraduate degree in horticultural therapy was awarded by Michigan State University in 1955.

As the American Horticultural Therapy Association likes to say, horticultural therapy harvests many benefits. Harvesting plants, whether indoors or out, can promote cognitive development, improve psychological outlook, promote social growth, and aid in physical rehabilitation.

Cognitive Uses. Growing plants teaches new skills and language, increases attention span, raises concentration levels, and improves the ability to work independently, solve problems, and follow directions.

Psychological Development. Because garden plants depend on people for care, nuturing needs are met through responsibility for something living. Successful projects encourage creativity and promote self-esteem and feelings of usefulness and responsibility. Activities such as hoeing, weeding, repotting, and pruning are also useful in helping to relieve aggressive feelings, tension, and stress.

Social Growth. Working in a horticultural therapy group encourages participants to compromise and share. These therapy groups increase social interaction.

Physical Rehabilitation. Gardening activities can be adapted to the individual's limitations and can provide an incentive to exercise and retrain muscles through the repetition of gross and fine motor activities.

LIGHT THERAPY

Although we don't often realize it, light has a profound effect on our mental and physical health. We use light to set our internal clocks and give us cues as to when to sleep and wake. Our skin uses the ultraviolet light from the sun to help manufacture vitamin D—a vitamin that research has shown to be necessary for building bone strength.

Rays from sunlight stimulate the pea-sized organ in the head known as the *pineal gland*. The light affects the gland's secretion of melatonin, a hormone that influences many bodily functions, including sleep, ovulation, and the secretion of other hormones. Light has been used to successfully treat a wide range of medical problems. The use of blue light, for example, is the standard treatment for neonatal jaundice.

In Scandinavia and Siberia—places where sunlight is hard to come by in the winter months—many children often undergo full-spectrum light therapy to ensure that their skin produces enough vitamin D for healthy bone development. Light boxes, which slowly increase the amount of light in the room in an approximation of dawn, are used to treat certain types of depression.

Syntonics, the therapeutic application of light through the eyes, has been used clinically in the field of optometry for more than 60 years in the treatment of a range of visual dysfunctions affecting general performance, behavior, and academic achievements. The syntonic approach involves prescribing different frequencies (colors) of light to stimulate and balance the autonomic nervous system.

The therapeutic approach of syntonics was conceived in the 1920s by Dr. Harry Riley Spitler based on his belief that the application of certain light frequencies by way of the eyes could restore balance within the body's regulatory centers. Today, the study of syntonics is available to all doctors of optometry as part of the postgraduate curricula.

Light's well-documented effect on brain chemistry has opened the door for its use in a wide range of neurologic disorders. It is also a popular therapy for certain dermatologic disorders and may have an application in cases of lupus erythematosus. Light therapy has been used to treat the following conditions:

Learning Disabilities. A study involving application of syntonics to 18 patients with reading difficulties resulted in unexpected substantial increases in visual fields. According to the study, published in the *Journal of Optometry and Vision Development* in 1986, most patients also reported greater release of emotions, less hyperactivity, less tension, and a greater ability to handle criticism and confrontation. What's more, 75 percent reported improved academic scores, 40 percent experienced significant improvement in handwriting, and 11 percent totally eliminated daily use of methylphenidate (Ritalin).

Psoriasis. Psoriasis is a skin disease that involves the uncontrolled growth of skin cells. This growth produces thick skin eruptions that cause itching and pain. A therapy called *PUVA treatment*—exposure to ultraviolet A (UVA) light after the administration of the drug psoralen, which heightens the body's sensitivity to ultraviolet light—may bring relief to some people with psoriasis. The benefits of light therapy need to be weighted against the risks of prolonged exposure to ultraviolet radiation, however.

Seasonal Affective Disorder. Seasonal affective disorder (SAD), one of the most common causes of depression, is directly caused by the seasonal lack of light experienced during the winter months by people who live in northern climates. SAD is one of light therapy's greatest successes. Many studies have shown that exposure to ambient light and its subsequent effects on the body's own melatonin production can ease the depressive symptoms of seasonal affective disorder.

MEDITATION

Humans beings have long been fascinated with the power of the mind to promote healing. Meditation might be defined as a mental exercise aimed at training the mind to let go and become free. Others have described it as learning how to stay anchored in the present moment or to quiet the mind. Many look to meditation as a way to enhance the mental, physical, or emotional aspects of their lives.

People who practice meditation regularly find they become more resilient to life's ups and downs. Frustrations, disappointments, and worries don't get to them as much; they feel better able to deal with whatever the day may bring their way. In addition, meditation also appears to affect the physiologic

responses that reflect emotional states, such as muscle tension and levels of brain chemicals called *neurotransmitters.*

Meditation has been shown to enhance physical, psychological, and emotional well-being. High blood pressure, pain, and anxiety disorders are but a few of the conditions that meditation can ameliorate. The key to successful meditation practice is to find a technique suited to you.

Meditation can take many forms. It may be sitting quietly and freeing the mind, but it does not have to be a stationary practice. Walking meditation involves walking while focusing attention completely on what the body is doing with every step. Even common daily activities such as washing the dishes can be meditative if you perform them attentively.

While meditation techniques are diverse, overall they can be grouped into two broad categories: concentration and insight. The concentration method focuses the attention on something, such as the breath, a candle flame, a sound, or a repeated word or thought (called a *mantra*). The insight technique (also called *mindfulness*) involves expanding awareness by opening up one's attention to assorted passing feelings, thoughts, images, sounds, and so on without reacting to them. The idea is to stay calm, just noticing whatever is there, without judging or getting emotionally wrapped up in it.

People who live with chronic pain face a daily challenge of coping. Pain in itself can be debilitating, but the depression that can accompany pain can also be extremely difficult to deal with. Drug therapy for these patients is often limited in effectiveness; meditation, however, may prove to be more helpful.

In a study of 51 chronic pain sufferers—ranging from back pain to chest pain (angina)—a form of mindfulness meditation was used in a ten-week outpatient treatment program. The technique involved "detached observation" of the pain, evaluating it as an observer, rather than experiencing it as a subject. After the ten-week program, 65 percent of the participants reported a significant reduction in their perceived pain; in fact, 50 percent said their pain was reduced by more than half. Significant reductions in mood disturbances and psychiatric symptoms accompanied the reduction in pain as well.

What's more, a recent study evaluated the effectiveness of a mindfulness meditation-based stress-reduction program for helping fibromyalgia patients cope with their disease. (Fibromyalgia is a chronic illness characterized by widespread pain, fatigue, and resistance to treatment.) All participants experienced at least some improvement, but 51 percent showed "marked to moderate improvement" in their symptoms.

Meditation can have significant effects on cardiovascular health, too. People with high blood pressure (hypertension) can experience dramatic improvement through several forms of meditation. Meditation may also have therapeutic value similar to regular exercise in improving actual physiologic changes in the brain related to mood. Researchers in the United States and Australia compared a group of runners with trained meditators to assess changes in levels of three hormones related to mood state. The research team found that hormone levels and moods were elevated in both groups, with no significant differences between runners and meditators.

For all of meditation's benefits, however, researchers have found that meditation can bring on some negative physical and emotional experiences. (Professional instructors should be used during the learning process.) Some of the reported problems that people experience include anxiety, depression, and even physical discomforts such as headaches, sore throats,

Meditation Tips

Find a quiet place and sit comfortably, with eyes closed and body relaxed. Pick a word, phrase, or image to focus on while you sit. Breathe slowly and naturally. If other thoughts, worries, and distractions come up, just gently brush them aside and return to your focus. Continue the meditation for about 20 minutes.

Here are a few general, basic ideas for helping you get the most out of your meditation:

• Make sure the place you pick is out of the way. It should be somewhere quiet, removed from distractions.

• Take on a comfortable physical position. It is not necessary to assume the lotus position to meditate; sitting or lying down is fine.

• Wear loose clothing.

• Relax and take on a passive attitude. Don't try to make something happen.

cramped muscles, sweating, shivering, trembling, racing heart-beat, and tingling or stinging sensations in parts of the body. Other side effects might include having certain smell or taste sensations or sudden laughing or crying outbursts. Some experts attribute these symptoms to tension release. Usually, these symptoms are only experienced by new meditators, who soon see the problems vanish. Such side effects are not indicators to stop or reduce meditation time—unless the effects persist and make you really uncomfortable.

(If you have conditions such as diabetes and high blood pressure, you may find that meditating causes changes in how much medication you need. Be sure to be monitored by a health professional who can advise you on any necessary medication adjustments.)

If meditation does appeal to you, try taking a class to learn some of the basic techniques. Private teachers, health care centers, fitness clubs, or community organizations in your area may teach classes in meditation.

A crucial first step is finding the meditation technique that's best suited for you. For instance, you may be someone who gets overanxious sitting still. Or if you're an analytical person, a more structured meditation might be the optimum fit, at least for starters. With a little investigating and experimenting, you'll find a technique that feels comfortable for you.

Regular practice each day, even if you don't feel like it, is key to deriving full benefit from meditation. And, as is the case with any sport or art form, don't expect to master meditation in a few weeks or months.

Don't get discouraged if your initial meditation sessions don't turn out as you'd hoped. It's only natural for the mind to wander, for distractions to pop up that steer you off track. Just remember, even people who have been practicing meditation for a long time still have an unsatisfying session now and then. So be patient. You will see the benefits in time.

YOGA

The word yoga comes from the Sanskrit word *yug*, meaning "to yoke, bind, join, or direct one's attention." Yoga is a centuries-old spiritual discipline originally practiced by Hindus and Buddhists to attain higher consciousness.

There are many different forms of yoga. Hatha yoga focuses on physical control and positions, while kundalini yoga is an attempt to open centers of psychic energy called *chakras*. You don't need to be Hindu or Buddhist to benefit from yoga; many people today practice yoga to attain bodily or mental control and well-being.

Although yoga has been shown to be beneficial in a variety of conditions, it is not considered a therapy for specific illnesses. Rather, yoga employs a broad holistic approach that focuses on teaching people a new lifestyle.

Studies show that people who practice yoga have reduced anxiety, are more resistant to stress, and have lower blood pressure, more efficient heart function, better respiratory function, and improved physical fitness. Yoga may also be useful in helping people with drug or alcohol addictions, cancer, heart disease, high blood pressure, and migraines. Yoga can relieve muscle tightness, joint pain, neck and back problems, muscle pulls, tendinitis, strains, and sprains. Other conditions that respond well to yoga include knee pain, sciatica, shinsplints, hamstring injuries, plantar fasciitis, stress fractures, and rotator cuff injuries. In addition to these physical benefits, yoga brings a calmness to the mind, thanks to the concentration and breath control it requires.

Correct breathing is a major aspect of yoga, serving to increase oxygen intake. In this way, deep, mindful breathing promotes mental and physical health, causing us to focus on our breathing rather than on our worries. The result of breath control is less stress and more energy.

Mental health and physical energy are difficult to qualify, but virtually everyone who participates in yoga over a period of time reports a positive effect on outlook and energy level. A

British study of 71 healthy volunteers aged 21 to 76, for example, found that a 30-minute program of yogic stretching and breathing exercises was simple to learn and resulted in a "markedly invigorating" effect on perceptions of mental and physical energy and improved mood.

The study, published in the *Journal of the Royal Society of Medicine* in 1993, compared relaxation, visualization, and yoga. It found that those who practiced yoga had a significantly greater increase in perceptions of mental and physical energy and feelings of alertness and enthusiasm than the other groups. Relaxation, on the other hand, was found to make people more sleepy and sluggish after a session, and visualization made them more sluggish and less content than those who practiced yoga.

Yoga movements are slow and precise. The movements stretch and tone the muscles while gently exercising the heart and lungs. As with any type of stretching, it's important to warm up before performing yoga movements. Yoga classes are generally widely available at gyms and health clubs.

HYPNOTHERAPY

Hypnotherapy is therapy using hypnosis—sometimes called the art of suggestion. Physical, psychological, and emotional disorders have been found to respond to hypnotherapy. Many medical doctors, dentists, psychologists, psychiatrists, and natural health practitioners are using hypnotherapy to treat conditions ranging from asthma and overeating to skin diseases.

Hypnotism may seem unfamiliar to most, but common experiences do give a glimpse of what the hypnotic state is like. On a long, boring car drive when suddenly you realize you have no recollection of what you've seen for the last several miles, or when you are so engrossed in doing something that you shut out everything else—these situations can be thought of as slightly hypnotic states.

The hypnotic state is not sleep, but it's also not a state of full wakefulness in the usual sense either. It lies somewhere in between. In fact, electroencephalography (EEG) shows that a hypnotized person's brain rhythm is in neither a waking nor a sleeping pattern. Still, no one can say for sure exactly how hypnosis really works. During hypnosis, the normally "in-charge" conscious mind somehow takes a backseat to let the subconscious come to the forefront.

Hypnosis is the inducing of the altered state described above. Hypnotherapy, on the other hand, is using hypnosis for therapy—to deal with some psychological, physical, or emotional condition or conflict. This therapeutic process becomes possible because while under hypnosis, a person is open to suggestion. New ways of thinking about the body, feelings, or abilities are opened up during hypnotherapy that rational, intellectual logic might normally reject.

Hypnotherapy experts are quick to point out that hypnotherapy cannot heal every condition, nor does it work for every person. Still, unlike the sideshow image that some people have of hypnosis, health professionals in diverse disciplines have found hypnotherapy useful. It's being used in psychiatry, psychotherapy, general medicine, and dentistry to treat conditions such as

- chronic pain
- pain during childbirth
- bed-wetting
- muscle spasms

The Road to Credibility

Although healing by suggestion has roots in almost every human culture, hypnosis has been through ups and downs in recent centuries in gaining credibility. A key shift came in 1955, when the British Medical Association approved hypnotherapy as a valid medical treatment. Three years later, the American Medical Association also granted its stamp of approval.

- asthma
- high blood pressure
- skin disorders
- headaches
- migraines
- ulcerative colitis
- anorexia
- anxiety
- pain and discomfort during dental procedures
- addictions (to alcohol and other drugs, smoking, overeating)
- inflammation
- nausea (such as from morning sickness or chemotherapy)
- irritable bowel syndrome
- weight problems
- sexual dysfunction
- phobias
- stress
- depression
- menstrual discomforts
- impaired immunity

One of the major clinical applications of hypnosis is in the management of pain. Chronic and episodic pain can often be ameliorated by hypnotherapy. In one case, published in the *Journal of Family Practice* in 1990, a woman suffering from painful attacks of sickle-cell disease was unresponsive to pain medication and other conventional interventions. Using a technique called *glove anesthesia*, she was able to obtain immediate relief. In this technique, the subject under hypnosis imagines her hand becoming numb in an ice-cold bucket of water, and the suggestion is given that the numbness can be transferred to any part of the body to numb pain.

People with other conditions such as arthritis that cause chronic pain can also benefit from this and other forms of hypnotherapy. Perhaps one of the more astounding uses of hypnotherapy has been as a substitute for anesthesia during minor and major surgery—a practice first employed by the French physician Jules Cloquet in 1829. It has also been used to aid in pain management and recovery after surgery and during the treatment of serious and painful burns.

In addition to the pain-management benefits that hypnotherapy can bring to women in labor, certain suggestion techniques can also be useful in focusing the mother's breathing and relaxation during labor. Maternal anxiety is associated with an increase in childbirth complications, and hypnotherapy may be able to influence the expectant mother to produce

Hope, Faith & Healing

a smoother labor. One study, published in the *Archives of Family Medicine* in 1994, found that hypnotherapy conducted in the weeks before delivery was able to turn fetuses in the breech position to the headfirst position.

Hypnosis is beginning to gain wide acceptance in the addiction-treatment community. In smoking-cessation programs, hypnotherapy has proved comparable to other treatment methods and is showing great promise as an adjunct to more conventional types of therapy.

Hypnosis can also be used to enhance relaxation, concentration, and creativity. This has become a popular use of hypnosis and self-hypnosis. For instance, athletes and business people use these techniques to bolster performance levels on the playing field or in the corporate office.

The following is a look at some of the many myths of hypnotherapy:

I'll lose control. It is only natural to be afraid to submit oneself to someone else's suggestions, but the fact is the patient remains in control at all times during hypnosis. That's why some hypnotherapy experts say that hypnosis is simply self-hypnosis. The patient actually chooses if and when to enter the hypnotic state and when to leave it. Furthermore, the power of suggestion only works with the patient's consent—if it's something that he or she truly wants to do. (You simply cannot be made to do anything against your will.)

I might get stuck in the hypnotized state. This cannot happen, hypnotherapists say. The patient retains the ability at all times to come back to full consciousness instantly.

If I can't be hypnotized, it must be my fault. Some people, for whatever reason, just don't take to hypnotic suggestion. That doesn't mean you're in any way deficient or lacking. Not everyone is "hypnotizable." The World Health Organization estimates that 90 percent of the population can be hypnotized, while other sources put it at about 70 percent. If you decide to try it, a qualified hypnotherapist can test you for suggestibility.

Working with the right hypnotherapist is a crucial part of successful treatment. Many states have no certification process for hypnotherapists. Inquire about the therapist's training and experience. Ask around for referrals in your community.

Trust and a good rapport are also key. Incompatibilities between the personalities of therapist and subject can quickly sabotage the chance for effective hypnotherapy. The hypnotherapist should be willing to take time to talk with you about any concerns you have about this form of treatment.

The other person qualified to perform hypnosis is you. In self-hypnosis, you act as if you are the hypnotherapist, after learning a few techniques. You might use self-hypnosis as an adjunct to working with a hypnotherapist, or you might decide to do it on your own. It's important that you feel comfortable with the latter idea, however, and not just pursue it to cut costs. Most hypnotherapists will teach their clients self-hypnosis techniques. And there is a wide range of literature on the subject, too.

ACUPUNCTURE

Used in China for thousands of years and in Western Europe for several hundred years, acupuncture came to America in the late 1800s. Sir William Osler's *Principles and Practice of Medicine*—an early American medical textbook, first published in 1892—recommended acupuncture for the treatment of lumbago, or lower-back pain.

Acupuncture is the insertion of tiny, hair-thin needles into specific points of the body. The Chinese believe that qi (pronounced chee), or vital energy, is responsible for health, and that an imbalance of qi results in illness. Acupuncture is used to correct the flow of qi to restore health and vitality.

Chinese medicine recognizes 12 major meridians, or pathways, for qi. Each of the 12 major meridians is associated with a vital organ or vital function. These meridians form an invisible network that carries qi to every tissue in the body. Acupuncture stimulates specific points along these pathways to rebalance a person's energy, or qi, by redirecting or stimulating it. Instead of needles, acupuncturists sometimes apply pressure (acupressure), heat (moxibustion), or suction (cupping) to the points. Western medicine has no direct parallels to the Chinese meridian system. Chinese practitioners believe that meridians provide links from the outside of the body to the body's organs, and that stimulation of these points can directly affect what is going on inside the body.

Chinese medicine is holistic, that is, it focuses on the entire patient, rather than a specific illness, organ, or symptom. Physical exams concentrate on detecting a pattern of disharmony or imbalance, and treatment seeks to restore balance through the use of techniques such as acupuncture, diet, or herbal medicine. Modern Western medicine focuses on finding a specific cause for an illness or disease and directing treatment toward its eradication.

An increasing number of scientists have tried to discover how acupuncture works from the viewpoint of Western science, and now a number of theories exist. Some believe acupuncture stimulates the release of endorphins, painkilling substances produced naturally by the body. Others say that stimulation from the needles interferes with normal nervous system pathways so that pain signals can't reach the brain. Still other studies suggest that acupuncture points have electrical properties that, when stimulated, alter chemical neurotransmitters in the body. Acupuncture may also alter the body's natural electrical currents.

In the United States acupuncture is widely used to treat lower-back pain and chronic pain. Its effectiveness in treating substance addiction has led some localities to mandate its inclusion in court-ordered rehabilitation programs.

Many people are uneasy about trying acupuncture for the first time. To Westerners used to conventional medicine's approach, the whole idea may seem a little strange. Some straightforward answers to the obvious questions should ease anxiety.

Most people feel only minimal pain as the needles are inserted. The tiny needles have smooth points and cause less pain than an injection with a hypodermic needle, which has a sharp cutting edge. Also, the needles are inserted into specific points on the body that are not the most sensitive areas.

A minimum of two needles are used, with the average number being six to eight needles. Sometimes, such as in the treatment of substance abuse, very short needles with a special circular end are covered with tiny specks of adhesive and left in place in the ear so patients can stimulate the point when they experience withdrawal symptoms.

Acupuncturists may also use very mild electrical energy to stimulate the meridian points further (eletroacupuncture). These electrical stimulation points may involve current passed to the points via small electrodes placed on the skin or through needles already inserted.

The number of treatments required varies from person to person and with the condition being treated. Complex or

Hope, Faith & Healing

chronic conditions may require one or two acupuncture treatments a week for several months.

Acupuncture is one of the most thoroughly researched and documented alternative medical practices in use today. A number of clinical studies have shown compelling evidence that it is an effective treatment for a variety of conditions.

After the Chinese Revolution in 1949, government officials intent on "modernizing" China took a hard look at acupuncture and other elements of traditional Chinese medicine. The state sponsored a staggering array of studies and analyses, some involving thousands and thousands of patients, before determining that acupuncture and traditional Chinese medicine deserved equal status with conventional Western medicine. Most physicians trained in China today learn both systems.

Many studies of acupuncture are published in Chinese or other foreign languages and have not been translated into English. Despite this limitation, a number of well-designed studies have been published in English and show the promise of acupuncture in treating a variety of conditions.

Alcoholism and Addiction. Acupuncture is often used for the treatment of alcohol and drug abuse. Research studies and clinical experience strongly suggest that acupuncture can play an important role in many substance abuse programs for persons addicted to alcohol, cocaine, heroin, nicotine, and

Hope, Faith & Healing

other harmful substances. In fact, acupuncture's high degree of success in these hard-to-treat areas has led some localities, such as New York City, to include the practice in many of its drug treatment programs.

One example of acupuncture's effectiveness in addiction treatment is a 1989 Minnesota study of 80 severe alcoholics. The patients who received "sham" acupuncture (not given at the correct points) were twice as likely to drink and be hospitalized for detoxification than those who received real acupuncture.

A study of 100 heroin addicts comparing real acupuncture to sham acupuncture found that persons who received real acupuncture attended the detoxification clinic more days and were more likely to continue beyond the 21-day detoxification period. Some clinical reports suggest that acupuncture may also be a useful adjunct to detoxification treatment for cocaine-addicted adults and children and for persons addicted to prescription drugs.

Arthritis. A Danish study of 32 patients awaiting knee-replacement surgery found that those treated with acupuncture showed improvement in knee function and had a 50 percent reduction in the use of pain medicine. In fact, 7 patients responded so well that they decided to not have the surgery at all.

Nausea. Acupuncture can be an effective way to stop nausea and vomiting caused by anesthesia, cancer therapy, motion sickness, and pregnancy. A study of 500 patients undergoing general anesthesia found that those who received acupuncture treatments not only responded better than those who received no treatment or sham acupuncture, but had slightly better results than those treated with the standard antinausea drugs.

How can acupuncture settle a sick stomach? Acupuncture controls nausea and vomiting by stimulating the P6 point above the wrist. A study of 130 patients undergoing cancer chemotherapy found that electrical stimulation of this point lessened symptoms of nausea in 97 percent of those treated.

The effectiveness of acupuncture, or acupressure, to this point has led to the development of sea bands—elastic wrist bands that contain a button that presses on the P6 point. Originally designed to eliminate seasickness, the bands have also been found to successfully reduce nausea after surgery and morning sickness in pregnant women.

Pain. Among patients with chronic lower-back pain, a 1980 study of 50 patients found that 83 percent of those treated immediately with acupuncture improved and took significantly fewer pain pills than those who were not treated. According to the study, published in the *American Journal of Chinese Medicine,* only 30 percent of the group that was not treated with acupuncture reported improvement.

In 1987, a study of 43 women suffering from dysmenorrhea (painful menstrual periods) found that 91 percent of those who received acupuncture showed improvement, compared with only 36 percent of the sham group. Published in *Obstetrics & Gynecology*, the study also found that patients who received acupuncture used 41 percent less pain medication than the control group.

Acupuncture may also help sufferers of migraines. A study of 30 migraine sufferers found that patients who received real acupuncture reported 43 percent less pain and used 38 percent less pain medication than those who received a method of sham acupuncture.

Patients with chronic neck pain may benefit as well. A study of 30 patients with chronic neck pain (pain that lasted an average of eight years) found that after 12 weeks of treatment, 80 percent reported improvement and took 54 percent less pain medication than before. Among patients who did not receive acupuncture, only 13 percent improved, and 60 percent worsened, according to a study published in 1982 in the *American Journal of Chinese Medicine*.

A study published in 1992 in the *Journal of Urology* found, of 38 patients experiencing pain from kidney stones, acupuncture was as effective as pain medication but without medication's accompanying side effects.

There are an estimated 7,000 acupuncture practitioners in the United States, more than half of whom are certified by the National Commission for the Certification of Acupuncturists. Naturopathic and chiropractic physicians often practice acupuncture, and more than 3,000 medical doctors and osteopaths have training in the practice as well.

Imagery is the process of imagining through any sense—hearing, sight, smell, taste, or touch. Sometimes the word imagery is used in the same way as visualization, but visualization refers only to seeing something in the mind's eye.

Imagery is commonly used as a technique to encourage changes in attitudes, behavior, or physiologic reactions. It is used in a wide variety of therapies and may also be used as a form of meditation. A number of therapies include imagery in their work, including

- autogenic training
- biofeedback
- desensitization and counterconditioning
- hypnosis
- neurolinguistic programming
- relaxation techniques
- Transcendental Meditation

Imagery can be performed in several ways (see box, page 225). The most common, perhaps, is simply to imagine a successful outcome to your situation. "Rehearsing" a surgery or difficult procedure before it happens helps patients to be prepared or to get rid of unrealistic fantasies. Patients are taught coping techniques such as abdominal breathing, distraction, mental dissociation, and muscle relaxation.

Imagery can also be used for diagnosis and evaluation by asking patients to describe their condition in sensory terms. In psychotherapy, for example, patients may be asked about their dreams to gain insight into a situation. From this imagery information a practitioner can provide the basis for mental rehearsal and therapy strategies.

Imagery can be used to help relieve pain and side effects from medical techniques. Imagery can be helpful in a variety of other situations, including the following:

Anxiety. A study of 51 patients undergoing abdominal surgery found that those who were taught guided imagery before surgery had less postoperative pain than those who were not trained in the technique. The patients who used imagery were also less distressed by the surgery, felt as if they coped with it better, and requested less pain medication than patients who did not practice guided imagery.

A study of 41 patients, published in *Holistic Nursing Practice* in 1994, found that those who listened to a guided imagery/relaxation tape before their magnetic resonance scan and used guided imagery during their scan had less anxiety and moved less frequently during the procedure than those who did not practice the techniques. (Magnetic resonance imaging is a di-

Types of Imagery

Components of imagery and visualization are used in a variety of therapeutic approaches. The following are some of the terms you may come across:

Creative Visualization. Popularized by Shakti Bawain in her 1979 book, *Creative Visualization,* this term refers to the use of mental energy to improve health and life situations through affirmation, exercises, and meditations to make positive ideas and concepts become a reality.

Guided Imagery. Guided imagery frequently employs audiotapes and other methods to help people imagine specific images or to imagine that their body's immune system is attacking cancer cells.

Interactive Guided Imagery. Interactive guided imagery seeks to enhance awareness of the unconscious imagery patients already have and help them learn methods to mobilize their innate healing abilities. For example, patients may be asked to close their eyes and imagine a picture that represents their problem. They may then be guided in an imaginary dialogue with the image to explore and reveal its meaning. Such images can provide information about the problem, as well as the person's beliefs, hopes, fears, and resources.

agnostic test in which patients must lie very still inside a cylindrical tube, sometimes for up to an hour. The procedure can be anxiety producing because of concerns about what the test may find. In addition, some patients may feel claustrophobic as a result of having to lie quietly inside the cramped machine for a rather long period of time.)

Cancer. A study of 38 cancer patients compared those who practiced imagery in combination with chemotherapy with those who did not. According to the study, the patients in the imagery group learned mental imagery techniques and were given two imagery audiotapes to listen to daily. After four months, those who practiced imagery were found to have significantly better function of cancer-attacking cells than those patients who did not practice imagery. Six months later, patients in both groups had significant increases in disease state, however. But, after one year, fewer patients in the imagery group had died (14 percent) than in the control group (36 percent).

A study of 154 women with early breast cancer compared those using relaxation therapy or relaxation plus imagery with a control group undergoing neither therapy. At six weeks, women in the relaxation plus imagery group were more relaxed than those who received relaxation training only, whereas the mood of women in the control group worsened.

Imagery has also been found to be effective in reducing symptoms associated with cancer chemotherapy. A study of 28

Help Yourself Quit Smoking

As any former or current smoker can tell you, quitting cigarettes can be an arduous task. In fact, many ex-smokers fail to stay off cigarettes even after completing smoking cessation programs. Relapse rates of 60 to 80 percent are common even for people who make it through such programs.

People who start smoking again identify stress as a major factor in their picking up another pack. Studies confirm that staying off cigarettes is closely related to the coping skills of the ex-smoker in dealing with stress. An Ohio study of 76 people who had successfully completed a smoking cessation program found that training in relaxation imagery results in significantly reduced stress and lower relapse rates. The study compared ex-smokers who were trained in imagery techniques with those who attended support groups with no imagery training. Imagery techniques used included positive images of improved health, thoughts to delay a return to smoking and to distract, and deep breathing and relaxations methods. After three months 72 percent of the imagery group had stayed off cigarettes and only 28 percent had relapsed, whereas 49 percent of the control group relapsed.

cancer patients undergoing chemotherapy found that those who used chemotherapy-specific guided imagery reported a significantly more positive experience with therapy than those who did not use guided imagery.

Postpartum Depression. Postpartum depression can be alleviated by imagery, according to a study published in the *Journal of Holistic Nursing* in 1995. A study of 60 first-time mothers found that those who practiced guided imagery during the first four weeks after delivery had less anxiety and depression and greater self-esteem than women who did not.

Imagery may be best known for its ability to help patients mobilize their immune system. A study of 45 college students, published in *Biofeedback and Self-Regulation* in 1990, found that guided imagery can increase antibody production. The study compared students who were taught to focus on the immune system and who were given a tape with guided imagery instructions with students who were not. Antibodies to fight infection were significantly higher in the therapy group than in the other subjects.

Imagery is practiced and taught by a wide variety of conventional and alternative health care professionals. In fact, much of the recent research on the use of imagery in healing has been conducted by doctorally-trained nurses.

PROGRESSIVE RELAXATION

If you suffer from insomnia or tension, you may find that progressive relaxation will help you to fall asleep and unclench those tight muscles. Progressive relaxation is a method of stress relief that can be used to relax your entire body.

To begin progressive relaxation, sit in a chair or lie down with your palms up, legs slightly apart. Close your eyes. From head to toes, you are going to clench and then release all the muscles in your body. Take 4 to 10 seconds to clench your muscles, 10 to 20 seconds to release them.

Start by tightening your facial muscles—wrinkling your forehead, tightly closing your eyes, and grinning widely. Then relax them completely. Take a deep breath and exhale. Continue the exercise by focusing your neck and shoulders. (To tense the neck, press your head back hard and touch your chin to your chest.) Take a deep breath and exhale. Following the shoulders, move to the arms, hands (bend them back at the wrist), chest, stomach, buttocks, legs, and toes. Finally, tighten your entire body. Then relax, inhaling and exhaling deeply. Stay relaxed for a few minutes, breathing normally.

Closely related to progressive relaxation is a technique called *mind and body relaxation*, which is a form of visualization. This technique is also beneficial for treating insomnia and general tension. To perform mind and body relaxation, lie on your back and close your eyes. Starting at the top of your head, silently tell yourself to relax. Imagine the muscles relaxing. Move down to the forehead and then the eyes, repeating the message to relax. Take a deep breath and exhale.

Move on to the neck, shoulders, upper arms, forearms, hands, and fingers. As you reach the fingers, imagine your body's energy flowing through the fingertips and palms. Direct the energy back up through your body to the base of your skull. There it will wait until you have completed the exercise. Continue to breathe deeply. Next, focus on your chest, stomach, and buttocks; at each area, repeat the message to relax.

Finally, move on to the thighs, calves, feet, and toes. At this point, imagine all the tension leaving your body while the energy is flowing through your feet. Direct the energy to the base of the skull, joining it with the energy from your upper body. Hold the energy there for a moment, then release it, feeling it all flow back, filling your body.

BIOFEEDBACK

It's not always easy for us to know whether we are truly relaxed. Biofeedback can give us an objective assessment of our state of relaxation. Depending on the situation, a biofeedback therapist may measure muscle tension, skin temperature, changes in sweat activity, pulse rate and force, or breath rate, volume, and rhythm. Biofeedback is based on the principle that any function that can be monitored and displayed (or "fed back") to a person can then be regulated by that person.

Biofeedback enables individuals to see how their breathing, posture, and thinking affect certain responses, such as heart rate. For example, when a person takes slow, deep breaths, the heart rate decreases. Thinking relaxing thoughts can also slow the heart rate. Biofeedback treatments can be customized to focus on a specific body part, such as an aching neck.

Modern electronic equipment can monitor internal responses and convert them to visual or auditory information that can then be used to regulate the response. The monitoring device used depends on what condition the patient is being treated for and the response to be regulated. For example, the biofeedback technician may use electroencephalogram (EEG) feedback to measure brain-wave activity. The resulting information relayed back to the patient is used to help him or her achieve a relaxation response.

A common form of biofeedback involves the measurement of muscle tension via electromyographic, or EMG, feedback. Electrodes are attached to the involved muscles to measure electrical energy from the patient. Information from the electrodes is fed into a small monitoring box that registers the re-

The Road to Biofeedback

When experimental psychologist Neal Miller proposed in 1961 that the autonomic nervous system—the part of the nervous system that we don't use consciously—was trainable, he was met with skepticism. Prevailing thought was that autonomic responses, such as blood pressure and heart rate, could not be controlled. In fact, medical dictionaries of the time defined autonomic as "not subject to voluntary control." Miller's groundbreaking work showed that these responses could indeed be controlled through instrumental learning.

sults either through sound or sight. For example, sound may vary in pitch as the function being monitored decreases or increases. Visual meters may vary in brightness as the response decreases or increases.

Biofeedback works best when patients can achieve a meditative state of deep relaxation. Many patients like biofeedback because it puts them in control over their health. Biofeedback therapists teach patients mental exercises to reach the desired result, such as muscle relaxation or contraction. As a result, patients learn to control their inner responses. Training time varies from person to person and depends on the disorder being treated. Training for some disorders requires eight to ten sessions before the patient can control his or her response without the help of a monitoring machine.

Biofeedback is used to treat some 150 conditions, and its use for some conditions has already gained widespread acceptance. For example, the American Medical Association has endorsed the use of EMG biofeedback training for treating muscle-contraction (tension) headaches.

Since 1961, there have been more than 100 books published describing biofeedback and its uses. While biofeedback has been demonstrated to be effective for a wide variety of disorders, it is more useful for some conditions than others:

Bowel Incontinence. A number of studies from across the world have shown biofeedback to be a highly effective therapy for adults and children who suffer from bowel incontinence. Patients learn to squeeze their anal sphincter through feedback from a monitor that measures sphincter pressure.

A study of 15 patients with bowel incontinence found that biofeedback helped improve the condition for 73 percent of the participants. Another study of 28 patients with bowel incontinence, published in 1995 in *Diseases of the Colon and Rectum*, found that 46 percent achieved excellent results, 28 percent had good results, but 25 percent did not improve after biofeedback therapy.

Constipation. Other studies show that biofeedback can also help people who suffer from severe constipation by teaching them to relax their anal sphincter. For example, a study of 26 children with chronic severe constipation compared standard medical care of enemas followed by laxative therapy and diet modification to standard medical care and biofeedback. Sixteen months later, parents of the children treated with biofeedback reported that the children had significantly less constipation and fewer painful bowel movements and used fewer laxatives than those who received standard care alone, according to an article published in *Biofeedback & Self-Regulation* in 1994.

Headaches. A study of 25 patients with migraine headaches compared biofeedback therapy with relaxation techniques not aided by biofeedback. The group trained in biofeedback had significantly less pain and used less pain medication than the other group, according to an article published in the journal *Headache* in 1995. Another study of 10 women who suffered from migraines found a significant decrease in migraine episodes after 16 semiweekly sessions. The decreases in migraine episodes continued after therapy as well.

Research suggests that tension headaches can also be treated by biofeedback using EMG feedback. A study of 26 tension-headache sufferers found EMG biofeedback to decrease headaches in 50 to 100 percent of those treated compared with only 37 percent of persons in a relaxation control group. (The variation reflects the possibility that the success rate may depend on where the electrodes are placed.)

High Blood Pressure. A study of 19 patients with high blood pressure found a significant decline in blood pressure among patients who received biofeedback therapy and muscle relaxation therapy; those who received muscle relaxation therapy alone actually tended to have increased blood pressure.

Pain. A study of 57 patients with chronic back pain and 21 patients who suffered from temporomandibular (jaw) pain and dysfunction found that patients who received biofeedback training had significant reduction in pain, according to an article published in the *Journal of Consulting and Clinical Psychology* in 1993.

Rehabilitation. Stroke patients commonly experience difficulties in walking due to alterations in their gait cycle and foot-drop on the affected limb. A study of 16 stroke patients showed how EMG biofeedback treatment successfully aided conventional physical therapy. The patients who received biofeedback showed significant improvements in walking, according to the article published in *Stroke* in 1994.

A review of eight studies that included 192 stroke patients determined that the use of EMG biofeedback is an effective method for neuromuscular reeducation. Other research suggests that biofeedback may also help patients who have difficulty swallowing (dysphagia) after a stroke.

Urinary Incontinence. Published in the *Journal of Urology* in 1995, a study of 64 women with urinary incontinence found that alternating biofeedback and intravaginal electrical stimulation resulted in complete recovery for 21 women, recovery sufficient to avoid other forms of treatment for 20 women, and no success for 23 women—an overall success rate of 64 percent.

Respiratory Function. Biofeedback has also been shown to improve breathing and lung function in patients who suffer from cystic fibrosis.

Biofeedback is used in many health care fields, including dentistry, internal medicine, pain management, physical therapy and rehabilitation, and psychology and psychiatry. There are more than 10,000 biofeedback practitioners in the United

Hope, Faith & Healing

States. The Biofeedback Certification Institute of America, created in 1981, maintains standards and certifies those who meet those standards. Candidates must have a relevant degree from an accredited institution of higher education and have had at least 200 hours of formal training in biofeedback.

MASSAGE THERAPY

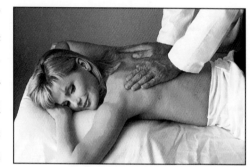

Massage therapy can be defined as the use of manual techniques to increase or achieve health and well-being. Massage therapy encompasses a variety of techniques that use touch to help the body heal. One of the oldest therapies in existence today, massage has been practiced for thousands of years. It is a major component of traditional Chinese medicine and is included as a therapy in the ancient Indian medical system known as Ayurveda. Its use in Western medicine dates back to the time of Hippocrates in the fourth century B.C.

Massage therapy is the systemized manipulation of soft tissues for the purpose of normalizing them. Practitioners use a variety of physical methods including applying fixed or movable pressure to the body. Therapists primarily used their

> ## Take Note
>
> Massage doesn't always come in handy. Don't massage:
>
> - Areas that are bruised, infected, inflamed, or swollen
> - If you suspect a broken bone
> - A person with a fever
> - A person with phlebitis or thrombosis
> - Tumors
> - Varicose veins

hands, but may also use their forearms, elbows, or feet. The basic appeal of massage therapy is to help the body heal itself and to increase health and well-being.

Touch is the core ingredient of massage therapy. Practitioners learn specific techniques for massage and use their sense of touch to determine the right amount of pressure to apply to each person and to locate areas of tension and other soft-tissue problems. Touch also conveys a sense of caring, an important component in the healing relationship.

Massage therapy has been shown to be effective in treating a variety of conditions including reducing anxiety, tension, and depression, promoting weight gain in low-birth-weight infants, and reducing pain caused by trauma.

Depression. In a study of children and adolescents hospitalized with depression, those who were treated with massage were found to be less anxious and depressed than those who viewed relaxing videotapes.

Pain. Massage has shown to be a cost-effective means of decreasing pain in patients with spinal trauma. In addition, a study of the use of massage in patients with pain from cancer found that those who received massage had a 60 percent lower level of pain perception and a 24 percent decrease in anxiety. More than half reported feeling more relaxed as well.

Premature Infants. Studies show that massage may even be beneficial to low-birth-weight infants. Premature infants treated with daily massage have been shown to gain more weight and have shorter hospital stays than infants who are not massaged. A Miami, Fla., study of 40 low-birth-weight babies found that 20 massaged babies had a 47 percent greater weight gain per day and stayed in the hospital an average six days less than 20 similar infants who did not receive massage therapy.

There are approximately 50,000 qualified massage therapists in the United States. The number of massage therapists is increasingly rapidly, with a corresponding increase in use by the public. Associations include the American Massage Therapy Association and the National Association of Nurse Massage Therapists. For more information on massage, check with your local library or bookstore.

Pattern recognition is one of the hallmarks of thought and consciousness. Most of the time, this ability to learn and use complex patterns of information and events is beneficial to our functioning in social and physical challenges.

However, certain patterns and modes of thinking can be negative, creating obstacles to the healing process and to well-being in general. Neurolinguistic programming can replace the patterns of association that limit the body's natural healing ability with patterns that promote wellness.

Neurolinguistic programming uses self-images and attitudes toward illness to effect change and promote healing. When a person feels helpless in the face of a chronic disease, for example, the body can stop trying to heal itself and the disease goes on unabated. However, when the patient learns to see the situation and his or her own abilities differently, the body can respond with powerful healing tools.

The neurolinguistic programming practitioner uses the verbal and nonverbal cues of the patient to diagnose (recognize) patterns of thought and develop strategies to repattern the patient's attitudes. By focusing the patient's mind on a state of health, programming activates the body's immune system to do the same. Furthermore, when both the mind and the body are aligned in a state of health, the patient's destructive behaviors are also more likely to be avoided.

Neurolinguistic programming has had anecdotal successes in treating life-threatening diseases such as AIDS and cancer, but controlled scientific studies are still lacking. Certainly, the technique's ability to enhance the body's own defenses to these illnesses and promote a happy mental attitude are advantages that, for some patients, may be worth pursuing.

Perhaps the therapy's greatest successes have come in the realm of mental health. Trauma, for example, can have negative consequences on mental health for years after. Neurolinguistic programming can help a person examine the memories of the event and change the harmful perceptions that continue to cause problems. One report of the technique's use involved an elderly patient diagnosed with clinical depression. By reviving positive memories, the practitioner was able to create a more positive self-image for the patient.

Practitioners of neurolinguistic programming receive certification from various organizations around the United States and Canada. For more information on neurolinguistic programming, visit your local library or bookstore.

DIET AND EXERCISE

Even when you're ill, you can't forget to eat right. When there's a small war going on inside you, you need a steady supply of ammunition—that is, nutritious foods—to hold your own. And, although your appetite may fall off, you should not skip meals or live on unhealthy foods. That can cause nutritional deficiencies and make you more vulnerable to all sorts of illnesses.

In general, you should try to tailor your diet to your medical history. No two people are the same. Their blood pressure, cholesterol level, and metabolic rate differ. Therefore, because you are different, it's best to learn all you can about your body before you develop a plan to improve your diet. If a physical exam reveals you have high blood pressure, for example, you will have to cut down on salty foods. You'll also need to limit your intake of fat and cholesterol. If you're allergic to milk, which is rich in calcium, you'll have to supplement your diet with other calcium-rich foods. If you're frequently tense or anxious, you may want to avoid products containing caffeine. If you have any questions about nutrition, be sure to talk to your physician. The more you know about your dietary needs, the better off your body—and your mind—will be.

If you're interested in improving your overall health, but alternative techniques such as imagery, meditation, or yoga just aren't for you, consider instead the stress-relieving effects of a regular exer-cise program. In addition to helping you banish tension from your life, exercise stimulates your mind, lowers your blood pressure, and helps you to sleep better. Of course, it also has other benefits, such as improved strength, flexibility, and muscle tone, all of which can boost your self-image. And a 10-year study conducted at the University of Wisconsin showed that regular intense exercise can dramatically slow the aging process.

So take up running, jogging, hiking, or walking the dog—all you need is a good pair of shoes. Swimming or weight training may require that you join a gym, but the tradeoff is that you will have access to a facility with a variety of equipment and classes. If you prefer not to leave the comfort of home, rent or buy an exercise video, follow along with one of the many televised exercise programs, or take up jumping rope.

Physical fitness and increased health are not the only benefits of starting and maintaining a lifelong fitness program. Various types of aerobic exercise, including walking, have also been found to promote mental health—boosting energy, improving sleep, relieving tension and stress, and combating anxiety and depression.

In fact, a few years ago, the National Institute of Mental Health (NIMH) convened a panel to examine the effects of exercise on mental health. The panel noted a real, proven link between physical fitness and mental health and well-being. Exercise was deemed generally beneficial for the emotional health of people of all ages and both sexes.

You might think that exercise is more likely to rev you up than calm you down, but you will soon discover that exercise leaves you with what can only be described as a feeling of relaxed euphoria. That feeling comes from increased blood flow to the brain, stimulation of the nervous system, and the release of endorphins—the body's own morphinelike substances—all combining to bring you a natural high that provides a general sense of good health and well-being.

INDEX

Hope, Faith & Healing

Hope, Faith & Healing

Hope, Faith & Healing

Hope, Faith & Healing